santiago

TRUE TALES of a
LITTLE BUG
in a BIG WORLD

JENNIFER VITANZO

Published by Late Shift Media, LLC
For publishing inquiries, visit our website at
www.lateshiftmedia.com

Paperback: 978-1-7337865-1-5
Kindle: 978-1-7337865-2-2
EPUB: 978-1-7337865-3-9
Library of Congress Cataloging Number: 2019935916
Library of Congress Cataloging in Publication data
on file with the publisher.

Disclaimer: The photographs in this story are copyrighted by
and the legal property of Jennifer Vitanzo. Please contact the
publisher for reproduction requests. The author and publisher
recommend that you consult with your local experts prior to
taking on any type of creature as a household pet.

Author photo by Neale Eckstein, www.NealeEckstein.com

Publishing and Production services provided by
Concierge Marketing Inc.
Printed in the United States of America.
First Printing 2019

10 9 8 7 6 5 4 3 2

Dedication

This book is dedicated to all the heroes who protect
the natural world and its inhabitants. Without them,
we would not have the air we breathe, the water we drink,
or the wildlife and wild spaces we love.

Please note: No one affiliated with this book advocates or condones taking
wild animals from the wild to keep as pets, nor do we support the exotic pet
trade. We ask that if you are interested in adding a pet to your family, that you
visit your local animal shelters. There are lots of loving animals there looking
for a forever home. Also, praying mantises do bite. You have been warned.

Contents

1

And So, It Begins

It only takes a moment to alter the direction of your life completely. What follows is an account of the series of adventures that I experienced after one such moment. Yes, it's a true story. Really.

You might wonder how a bug knows as much as I do about the world. Well, to that I say, never assume or underestimate anything in life. Plenty of big surprises come in the form of small packages.

My story began in summer. I, a newly hatched praying mantis, perched beneath the pink petals on a hydrangea bush, lazily watching the drops of sunlight as they fell through the tiny spaces between petal and leaf. I often hid under the petals of the hydrangea flowers, where I—being bright green and tiny—blended in perfectly with the rest of the bright green around me.

The constant buzzing of my neighbor, a chatty but lonely cicada who didn't seem to understand the concept of "quiet time," was so loud it vibrated along my perch and through my little body. I tried to explain to him that making so much noise attracted unwanted attention from dangerous creatures like birds, but he didn't care. He was on a mission to find the love of his life. I could only wish him luck.

The cicada was always buzzing, which annoyed other neighbors but didn't bother me. I liked the consistency of his buzzing.

It made it easier for me to keep track of where he was, unlike the bees and the flies, which you could only hear when they were nearby. It would be quiet, quiet, quiet, and then… BOOM! They'd pop up in your face, seemingly out of nowhere. I didn't like things sneaking up on me like that, suddenly there and then instantly gone again. But I could always tell where the cicada was. He never shut up. I'm pretty sure he even buzzed when he slept. If he ever slept. Which it didn't seem like he did.

My hydrangea bush was one of many that lined a long stone-covered path leading to a huge grassy area filled with lots of flowers, a handful of towering old trees with big, broad leaves, and rows of neatly trimmed shrubs of various sizes. At the end of the path was a big stone object where sunbirds often sat and chittered about the latest garden gossip, their green and red bodies shimmering like millions of gemstones in the sunshine.

Beyond the stone object was a separate area that was also green. But unlike the rest of the green area, this section was surrounded by a chain-link fence, and it was flat and decorated with white lines. Across the middle of this area hung what looked like a kind of giant spider web strung between two skinny silver stumps. People would run back and forth on the flat area, swinging wide paddles to smack a bright yellow ball back and forth over the web.

I have to say, the yellow ball made a very satisfying "ping" every time it connected with a paddle. Aside from that nice sound, though, the whole process seemed a waste of energy to me. We mantises don't waste energy. Apparently, people do. They were out there, smacking around that ball every few days. Except in the rain. No one did anything in the rain in Cape Town, where I lived. Well, to be more precise, I lived in Constantia. But regardless of my exact location, no one here went out in the rain if they could help it.

I think somewhere beyond that green space with the giant spider web was something called a pool. I'd heard a bee buzzing about it to another bee, but I never saw it. It was a gathering space for all the garden animals. Even the local porcupines visited. The big white building in the middle of the green spaces blocked my view, though, so I couldn't see it. It wasn't safe for me out by a pool anyway—too much open ground and too few hiding places for a tiny bug. And I heard pools were full of water. I didn't like water, not to mention I didn't know how to swim. We mantises are not swimmers.

Anyway, back to my lazy afternoon.

There I was, comfortably tucked among the petals and leaves of my hydrangea, listening to the cicada sing his love song, and daydreaming about fat grasshoppers.

Suddenly, I felt a violent jolt, and a huge, dark figure was standing before me. Terrified, I held tight and hoped that I would go unnoticed. The bush, whose branch I was sitting upon, whipped frantically back and forth. I heard a crack, and then I (and my branch) went speeding off into the unknown. Everything whizzed and bounced past me in streaks of blues, greens, pinks, and browns. I clung to the little pink petals, hoping I didn't get catapulted off.

DID YOU KNOW? Praying mantises do not like to swim.

The branch and I changed direction and up, up, up we went, heading straight into the sky. Then something flashed, a huge opening appeared, and into a shady, enclosed space I went. Immediately afterward I found myself in what looked like a white- and cream-colored cave. The sky was gone, replaced by white lines above me and yellow walls around me. There were several squarish openings where sunshine punched through the dim. And there were a few large objects, all in varying degrees of neutral colors, that I had never seen before.

There were no trees. No bushes. No flowers. Well, none except for the one I was sitting on. There were no clouds. No wind. No chirping birds. No buzzing insects. No sound at all, except for a soft humming coming from a spot low to the ground, which I could only assume was the rumbling of some strange new creature. I hoped that whatever it was, it didn't eat praying mantises.

The means of my rapid transportation from the garden to this new place was a female human being. I was well camouflaged and tiny, so when she cut the branch with the flower I was on, she didn't even know I existed. In fact, there were two of us sharing that branch that day: Myself and another slightly smaller mantis nymph. We both managed to hold on for dear life, and we both ended up in the cave. (Nymphs are what you call baby mantises, by the way.)

arriving via the hydrangea

2
Discovery

The human only discovered the presence of her two tiny stowaways after a few sunrises and sunsets. Noticing that some of the flower petals from one of the branches she'd cut began moving by themselves one day, she gently turned over the petals. There I was, my two big green eyes staring up at her, my little front legs folded up like I'd been in the middle of prayer. That's where we get our names from, by the way—we're called praying mantises because we curl our front legs up in a way that looks as if we are praying.

The human let out a tiny "ooop" sound.

I didn't move, hoping maybe I blended in enough with my surroundings for her not to notice me. But I knew better. She was staring straight into my eyes. She was not fooled.

Another tiny shudder from under another flower revealed my smaller fellow stowaway. Now we were both exposed.

I had never been this close to a human. It was equally terrifying and fascinating. They were so much bigger up close, and they had very different features from all the other animals I knew, except for maybe baboons. I had seen a baboon. There was a troop that lived in our neighborhood, though I usually only heard them rather than saw them. The humans chased the baboons when the baboons got too close to human caves, so the baboons—like so many other animals, including me—tended to stay hidden.

Though there were clear differences in looks, there were also so many similarities that made me wonder if maybe humans and baboons might be distant relatives. This human had a baboonishly long nose, and she had funny, baboon-like ears. But she was taller than any baboon I'd ever seen and had way less hair on her body.

The human stared at me and my fellow nymph mantis, looking back and forth at each of us and scrunching up her mouth parts. Then her mouth parts stretched to the sides, exposing what looked to me like a hundred teeth. My first thought was that they were almost blindingly white. My second one was that this was the end. She was going to eat us.

But she didn't. She closed her mouth parts over her teeth and let out a soft "hmmmph." It seemed she wasn't sure what to do. Maybe humans don't eat mantids? I realized at that moment that I knew a lot about the animals in the garden, but I knew very little about the human animal.

I took a quick look around me and sized up my options for escape. Even though I was fast, I knew there was no way I'd be able to run away fast enough without her easily catching me. She was about 100 times my size. All she needed to do was reach out her paw and grab me.

I chose to stay put. The other mantis, I noticed, was frozen in fear. I tried to get his attention by wiggling my antennae, but he ignored me. I wonder if he thought he was still camouflaged.

Oddly enough, despite my fear, looking at him suddenly made me feel hungry and I realized I hadn't eaten in a few days. I would have to fix that soon.

Though I was also afraid, I desperately wanted to say hello to the human. My instinct was telling me that something about her seemed safe. But I couldn't speak human. So, we just continued to stare at each other for a little while longer, each of us studying the other and not knowing what to do next.

The human let out another "hmmmph" and walked to the entrance of the cave. Then she looked back at us. Then back at the garden. She said another "hmmmph".

She started speaking to herself, wondering aloud if we would survive on our own—something I took offense to, since we praying mantises are totally self-sufficient from the moment we are born. But I guess she didn't know that. And I couldn't get mad at her for caring enough to worry about our survival, especially since she had only just met us.

DID YOU KNOW?

Praying mantises are totally self-sufficient from the moment they are born. This means that they are born with all the skills they need to survive.

Not only that, we came in on one of several hydrangeas branches she'd cut from several different overgrown bushes lining the long stone path. She muttered something about not knowing what part of the path we came from. It didn't matter; we mantises move around and don't have to stay in just one place. But I guess she didn't know that. I think she may have felt responsible for us now that she'd relocated us. And she apparently had no intention of eating us or I think she would have done that by now.

To be honest, though, I initially didn't really care what she was talking about. Until she said one word: "Mom."

Mom. I hadn't learned the human language very well yet. But I did know "*mom.*" And that word worried me. Even though I didn't know my biological mom, I knew what a mom was, and it's fair to say that some moms in the animal kingdom are definitely better at raising their children than others. My biological mom would NOT get the award for "Most Nurturing Parent." We'll come back to why later.

Did this human intend to be our new mom? Given our short interaction so far, she seemed to be both caring and non-threatening, which made me think her mom tendencies might travel the more nurturing track.

After a few moments of talking to herself, she sighed and said, "You are just babies. I will take care of you."

I don't know about the other mantis, but after taking a look around and realizing there were no birds here, I made up my mind. I was perfectly happy to stay in "the cave" with her rather than face the monsters—and there were many— that lurked in the garden.

My fellow mantis didn't last long. As I mentioned before, I got hungry. He was the closest game in town. Food is food, and when you're a small thing that's on the menu for just about every other animal, you take what you can get, even if it might be a distant cousin. Or even a sibling. And this is why I never knew my biological mother and why she would never win that Nurturing Parent Award. She didn't stick around for the birth of her own babies, and that's lucky for us, as she probably would've eaten half—if not all—of her kids had she been present on the day we were born. Wriggling out of the egg-filled sac she laid (it's called an ootheca, for anyone taking notes, and it's an amazing piece of construction), we likely would have been picked off for meals, one by one. Life for a praying mantis is a constant battle for survival.

DID YOU KNOW?

An ootheca is an egg case made by the female praying mantis to house and protect her eggs. It can contain hundreds of eggs!

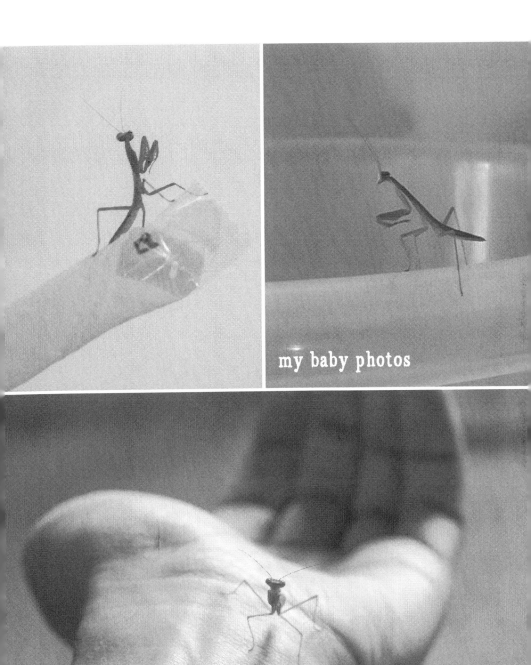

my baby photos

My mom drew a picture of my anatomy

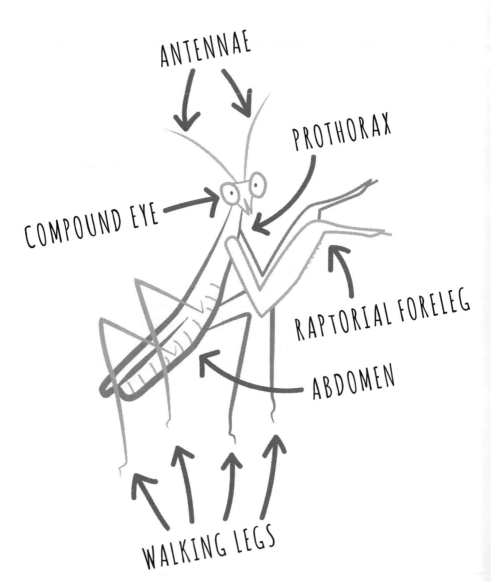

ANTENNAE

PROTHORAX

COMPOUND EYE

RAPTORIAL FORELEG

ABDOMEN

WALKING LEGS

3

A Little About
Praying Mantises

I'm not sure how much you know about praying mantises, so here's a little background for you before we get on with my story. Mantises are part of the insect family, which is the most diverse group of animals in the world. And yes, insects are animals. We are as much a part of the animal kingdom as a goose or a trout or a Komodo dragon. Or a human.

Mantises are part of a group called the arthropods. Arthropods are animals with a hard outer skeleton called an exoskeleton. Arthropods don't have backbones and are scientifically classified as invertebrates.

Humans have an internal skeleton and are, therefore, NOT arthropods. They also have a backbone, so they are scientifically classified as vertebrates.

However, though mantises have a hard exoskeleton, inside our tough exterior, we are total softies, like many other animals.

Want to know what other animals are arthropods? Lobsters, tarantulas, millipedes, and barnacles, to name a few. One might say that, given our numbers and variety of species, arthropods are an extremely successful group.

Unlike humans, mantises are cold-blooded and prefer warmer climates. We need sunlight to stay warm, which explains my obsession with finding safe places to sit that also provide access to plenty of sun.

Now that we have my lineage cleared up, let's look closer at the appearance of praying mantises (since this is, after all, a book about one). Mantises are like all insects in that we have three parts to our bodies—a head, thorax, and abdomen—and three sets of jointed legs (six legs in total). The joints work similarly to the way a human knee or shoulder works, allowing the limbs to bend. Like the three-part body, having six jointed legs is a trademark feature of insects, as is having antennae. Our antennae are like little radio towers, taking in frequencies and interpreting the messages they send. They help us detect prey and avoid predators.

DID YOU KNOW?

Mantises are part of a group called the arthropods. Arthropods are animals with a hard outer skeleton called an exoskeleton. Arthropods don't have backbones and are scientifically classified as invertebrates.

We don't have wings at birth, but, like most insects, many mantis species (including mine) do eventually develop them, so I would be able to fly when I got old enough. Until my wings sprouted, though, I was stuck walking on my six wiry legs.

If you want to know how it all breaks down, here is how the praying mantis family tree stacks up against humans.

PRAYING MANTIS	FAMILY TREE	HUMAN
Animalia	KINGDOM	Animalia
Arthropoda	PHYLUM	Chordata
Insecta	CLASS	Mammalia
Mantodea	ORDER	Primates
Mantidae	FAMILY	Hominidae
Depends on the mantis	GENUS	Homo
Depends on the mantis	SPECIES	Sapiens

4

Our Extended Family

As I mentioned before, mantises come from the order Mantodea, which includes over 2,400 different species of insects. We mantids make up the largest family (Mantidae) within that order.

Our cousins are cockroaches and termites, which makes an already difficult life that much more difficult for us, since many people don't seem to like bugs in general, and no one seems to like cockroaches and termites in particular. In fact, when others hear we are related to them, they don't always like mantises, either. I'm not sure why. Cockroaches are perfectly nice insects. And they have exceptional survival skills. Even better than mine, though I'll never admit it to them because cockroaches are excessively competitive. In fact, I've heard a few boast that they'd be the last living things on the planet if we had a massive species extinction. I have no idea what extinction is. I don't think I want to know, especially if it means there will be nothing but cockroaches left.

There's no point in arguing this, though. Since cockroaches seem to live forever, it just becomes a never-ending debate with them.

I understand why people don't like termites. Many eat wood, which sometimes means they eat people's caves (many of which are made of wood, I learned). I get why that would be a turn-off for humans. I can't imagine it would be fun to have your cave fall on you because some tiny bug chewed through the structure that holds your home together.

Some termites live in the ground and create massive underground tunnel systems, which can cause the ground to cave in. Which humans also don't like. And I don't blame them for that, either. Termites can be a bit of a nuisance, really. And they do bite. I've been bitten by one. It hurts. But I was trying to eat it, so I can't exactly fault it for biting me.

Aside from causing massive destruction and being rather bite-y, though, termites are quite harmless.

5

He's Got...Personality!

A s far as personality goes, mantises aren't the friendliest animals in the world. You definitely won't find us invited to many insect gatherings. We don't hold grudges about this, though, as we think not being on the invite list is understandable. We are, after all, carnivorous, which means we eat meat—in my case, other insects and small spiders. (Oh, and if you're interested, spiders aren't insects. They fall into their own classification called arachnids, which they share with scorpions, ticks, and mites.) There are even some praying mantises that eat lizards, small mammals, and birds, but they are big mantises, much bigger than I would ever be. Most of us stick to eating smaller prey. Either way, we'd be likely to eat at least one other guest at any insect party we attended, which doesn't exactly win us many friends (or invitations).

We are also solitary, ambush predators. We prefer to stay hidden so: 1. We keep our advantage when it comes to hunting prey, and 2. We don't get eaten. We don't go frolicking about and announcing our presence. Except for orchid mantises. They are, well, they are what one might call "flashy." Orchid mantises come in colors like bright pink and white, and they perch boldly on the ends of branches, posing as flowers, just begging passing bees to come by and mistake them for something to pollinate. Then they pounce on the bees. Or whatever else they manage to grab.

I don't do that. I mean, I do pounce on my prey. But I prefer to live incognito. I think the saying is "to each their own."

Mantises have a reputation for being very focused and patient. We move slowly and deliberately, swaying like branches in the breeze as we sneak up on our prey. Then, once we are within striking distance, we snatch our prey with astonishing speed. Our forearms are armed with sharp spikes, so once we let those puppies rip and grab hold, very few creatures can get away.

We use a similar approach as a cougar or a leopard when we attack—we try to bite the neck first and paralyze our prey. And because we have powerful mandibles (I think you humans call them jaws), we can break through the hard exoskeleton of other insects.

I think my human mom was equally disgusted and fascinated the first time she saw me stalk and kill a cricket. I'm not sure she ever got comfortable with having to find and serve me live meals. But mantises are excellent hunters, so once we strike we usually make short work of whatever we catch. Except for grasshoppers. Grasshoppers always take forever to eat.

It takes a while for others to get used to our ruthless methods and detached personalities, I know. One or two of my mom's friends who met me and saw me eat another bug gagged at the sight. But that's nature. Not always pretty, sometimes harsh, but definitely efficient and effective.

Our biggest enemies are birds, frogs, snakes, spiders, and (for those of us who travel around at night) bats. Oh, and other mantises, of course. And some humans. Why humans? Apparently, some of you like to kill bugs for fun, though I don't understand why that would be fun for anyone (and it certainly isn't fun for the bug).

Anyway, we are not known for our cuddliness or our friendship, mostly because of our habit of eating our friends. We travel solo.

me after having crickets over
for dinner

6

Figuring Out My
Place in the World

The first days of my life before moving to the cave were a quick learning curve. I had to focus on two things— eating and staying alive. If it moves and is smaller than you, grab it and eat it; if it moves and is larger than you, run away and/or hide!

As I mentioned before, I lived in Constantia, a small town in the country of South Africa. But I wasn't a South African mantis. I knew this for several reasons. First, all the other mantis nymphs in our garden looked very different to me. They were either white or straw colored. I was bright green.

Second, when my human mom tried to identify my species, she couldn't find any South African species that matched my description. The closest thing she found to a mantis that resembled my size and coloration was a Madagascan marbled mantis (Polyspilota aeruginosa is our Latin name, for anyone who cares). I was an import from Madagascar. Or at least my parents or grandparents were.

I don't think anyone was complaining about my being there, even though I wasn't South African. At least no one ever said anything to me about it. I'd like to think I was providing a valuable service by eating other insects that might otherwise kill the plants in the garden. I kept humans from needing to use chemicals like pesticides.

But sometimes introduced mantids DO cause problems. In fact, animals and plants introduced in areas where they don't belong are called invasive species. They can be destructive and outcompete the local flora and fauna. (Well, they can outcompete everything but the cockroaches. Apparently, nothing outcompetes them.)

Invasive mantids can be a big problem because mantids aren't picky about what insects they eat—they'll just as easily chow on bugs and other animals that are good for a garden as those that aren't. That's why it's so important to be very careful about introducing wildlife and plants in places where they don't naturally live. I heard about a country called Australia that has a major problem with something called a cane toad, which was introduced there and caused all kinds of problems for the local wildlife. And nothing could eat it because its skin was toxic and would poison anything that tried.

Even animals that seem harmless, like rabbits and goats, have caused lots of damage in places where they were introduced. I mean, goats eat everything. And they climb trees!

It's possible that, even though I didn't want to admit it, I might have been one of those problem animals. Luckily, I was only in the garden for a short time. There was a very limited amount of damage I could do.

For the first two (or maybe even three—who's counting?) weeks of my life, I lived on one hydrangea bush. I didn't need to move much because dinner often came to me. Life wasn't very exciting, except for the occasional times when danger appeared and I needed to hide. But because I learned to blend in quickly, could stay perfectly still, and had excellent eyesight, I spotted danger easily, but danger rarely seemed to spot me. Thankfully. In fact, I probably had more close calls once I moved into the cave than I did in my few short weeks in the garden. The garden didn't have a hot stove in it, for example. Or dust bunnies that clung like glue to every one of my six legs.

But the garden also didn't have my new mom.

I didn't get to know any of my siblings. We were never going to be a close family, though, since we might be inclined to eat each other.

In fact, a mantid's life can be very lonely. We eat everything, so no one wants to be our friend, which is understandable. But still. We all like to have at least one buddy. That's another reason I was happy to move to the cave. My mom kept me company. She didn't seem interested in eating me, and I wouldn't eat her, a perfect arrangement for all parties involved.

DID YOU KNOW?
Animals and plants introduced into areas where they are not native are called "invasive species."

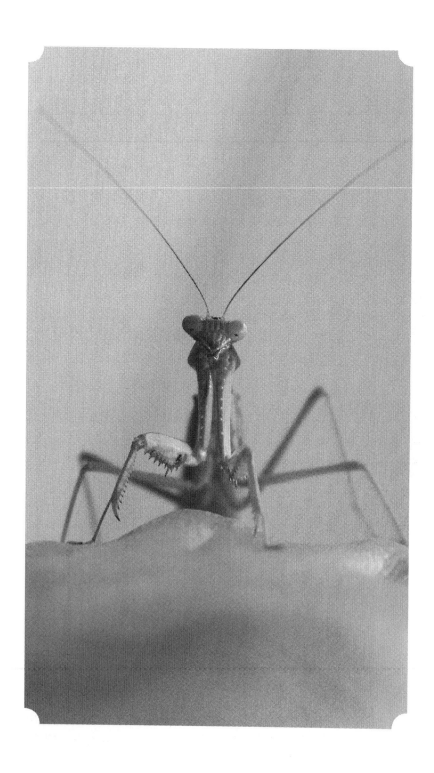

7

Got a Name?

Wait up! I've been telling you all about me, but I haven't introduced myself yet. How rude of me! I'm so sorry about that.

My name is Santiago. Yes, I am a South African (well, technically Madagascan) praying mantis with a Spanish name. My dad is the one who named me, which is strange since it's my mom, not my dad, who speaks Spanish. I have no idea where the name came from, and he took a chance with it because I was still a nymph when they named me. You can't tell a mantis's gender until it is fully grown, so my parents didn't yet know if I would be a boy or a girl. But luck was with my dad, as I did end up being a boy. Although I guess you could name a girl "Santiago" as well.

From the moment they named me, they started a tradition whereby all the insects they found in the cave got Spanish (or, as my mom said, Spanglish) names. Gringo, Fernando, Juanita. I have no idea why. It just was. And I was Santiago. I liked it.

I'm fairly certain I was the only praying mantis in South Africa named Santiago.

You might be wondering how to tell female and male mantises apart. The main way to do so is to flip us over and count the segments in our abdomen. Females have 6 segments while males have 8. Male mantises also generally have a slimmer abdomen and longer antennae and wings than females. So now you know.

8

Leaving the Garden

I moved into the cave on a beautiful summer day in mid-December (I lived in the Southern Hemisphere, where December is a summer month). It was the week before a holiday known as Christmas, which I learned was about many different things, depending on who was describing it: a little baby boy born in a barn-type place; the giving of lots of presents and eating of lots of food; and/or a big, fat man in a red suit who rode around on something called a sleigh and who liked to eat cookies. And I think there was something about a reindeer with a big red nose. We didn't have reindeer in South Africa, so though I tried, the only thing I could imagine was the red nose.

I didn't quite have a handle on understanding humans yet, so for a while, I had to rely mainly on instinct and my knowledge of body language. That meant at first, I only got bits and pieces of what was going on. Plus, during the first two weeks in the cave, I was still very shy and stayed far away from my mom and dad. In fact, after being discovered, I spent almost the entire first week at the top of the cave, which was a safe space far out of anyone or anything's reach.

I also tried to stay away from that humming thing on the ground, which I realized was not an animal at all. It was a white block my mom called the fridge. Given the cold air that it blew out every time its dark, cavernous mouth opened, I assume "fridge" was short for frigid, which I thought was a very appropriate name.

The fridge hummed all day and night. Eventually, I learned to just ignore it.

My human would occasionally feed it, and then later take things from its mouth and eat what she took out. I knew that some adult animals, like birds, regurgitate their food to feed their babies. Did the fridge regurgitate food for humans? The stuff they put into it looked the same going in as it did coming out, though, so the fridge didn't chew it up. What, then, was its purpose? To just sit there and hold food in its mouth?

I'd heard there was a fish that would scoop all its babies into its mouth when danger was near, but the fish didn't eat its babies. When danger moved on, the fish would spit the babies back out unharmed. But just holding food in your mouth for the sake of holding it there? I'd never heard of anything doing that before. In the wild, aside from that one particular fish species, when you end up in something's mouth, you usually don't come back out again. Especially not in one piece. This was a very strange world I now lived in.

Whatever the arrangement was, the fridge suited my human. She liked it. I did not. I stayed away from it. I didn't like the cold anyway.

However, there was also no food available at the top of the cave, so eventually, I would have to come down closer to the fridge and my human for a snack. Which I did the day I met my human dad.

9

Meeting My Dad

My human dad wasn't around for the first few days of my arrival because he worked far away from where we lived. I knew of him because I'd heard my mom talking to him on a thin little white rectangular object she held to the side of her face and spoke into. She called it a phone. She asked him plenty of questions about me. I guess he knew a lot about insects.

Much as I tried to imagine what he would look like, I really wasn't sure what to expect. Would he also look like a baboon's relative? Yup, he did. But with a smaller nose. He was much taller than my mom. And he had blue eyes. But otherwise, he and my mom had a lot of the same features. Though he was a lot hairier than she was. And the hair on his head was shorter.

He also talked differently than she did. They said the same words, but they sounded different coming from him. My mom said it was because the two of them were born in different countries, and even though they spoke the same language, they pronounced words differently. He was born in South Africa. My mom was born in the United States. Wherever that is.

None of this really mattered to me, though. All I cared about was that my dad wouldn't eat me and whether or not he could catch food for me. Luckily for me, my dad was a champion when it came to catching crickets and flies. Oh, and he didn't eat me either. So, points to him.

10

My First Assisted Feeding

The first day with my dad went like this: I was minding my own business on the ceiling, watching the scene below me and studying him. While my attention was on him, my mom crawled up onto the ledge below me and, after several attempts, managed to cup her hands around me, very gingerly moving me down from the top of the cave and onto the wooden ledge in front of one of the holes that overlooked the garden (she called the hole a window, and it opened and closed when she wanted it to). This particular window was in a place she called the kitchen.

She placed me gently on the ledge and backed away.

I sat mesmerized by this window thing. Since arriving, I'd either spent my time on the hydrangea plant or on the ceiling. This was the first time I really got a proper look at the window. So strange and fascinating! It was solid as a wall, but clear as water. I could see right through it!

The window was even more appealing because it gave me an unobstructed view of the garden and all its inhabitants while also providing me with a safe lookout to watch all the action. Nothing could get to me through this barrier. I could sit and watch birds all day without worrying about them carrying me off as a meal.

The window quickly became my new favorite place in the cave.

While I was admiring this window thing, my dad had gone out to the garden and caught a small cricket, brought it inside, placed it in front of me on the ledge, and waited. And waited. And waited.

At first, I wasn't sure what they were waiting for, as I was otherwise engaged looking out the window. I didn't even notice the cricket. And then my dad nudged it a little bit to get it to hop.

That did it.

Immediately, my attention turned and focused on the source of the movement. The window could wait.

It didn't take long for me to sneak up and pounce on the cricket. Dinner served.

For the next week, crickets and other assorted insects appeared on the ledge constantly, courtesy of my dad (and, occasionally, my mom).

Then, as suddenly as he appeared, my dad disappeared. But, thankfully, the food supply did not. During his visit, he had taught my mom how to catch insects in the garden so she was also able to supply me with a constant stream of snacks.

After my dad left us, my mom explained that my dad worked in "the bush," which was far from where we lived. This meant he would not be in the cave very often. She said the bush was a place filled with many amazing creatures like elephants and lions and hyenas and rhinos. We didn't have those in Constantia. But we had our own amazing animals, I thought. Including me.

I will never understand why so many people don't pay closer attention to and appreciate all the life right in their own back-yard. You don't have to travel very far to see fantastic wildlife. You only need to look out your window. If there's a tree, there's something worthwhile living in it. Even the tree itself is magi-cal. I mean, how cool is it that something so huge comes from a teeny, tiny seed?

Anyway, when my dad left, it was just my mom and me again, which is how it was most of the time.

11

Raising a Baby Mantis

In addition to asking my dad lots of questions, my mom read everything she could find that might help her with raising a praying mantis. What do we eat and how often? How long do we live? What type of environment do we need to live in? So many questions. Neither she nor my dad ever wanted to put me in a cage, so she came up with creative ways to keep me warm and feeling safe without putting me in some bug box. But first she had to earn my trust so she could catch me to relocate me. After all, as I said, she was about 100 times my size. She could easily crush me. And I still wasn't entirely sure she wasn't just fattening me up so she could eat me.

It took her about a week, but eventually she figured out that the best way to move me from point A to point B was to put her hand down in front of me and softly nudge me onto that hand by tapping my butt with her other hand or with a small stick or the end of a small metal branch.

She was always very gentle and didn't ever try to keep me from moving about, as she seemed to understand that if I was moving it was because I was scared, needed to find a place where I felt safe, and would keep moving until I did. With that in mind, she would let me climb up her fingers, constantly stacking her hands one above the other so I could keep climbing while she moved me to where she wanted me to go. Once we got there, she would lay her hand flat and let me crawl off onto whatever drop-off point she'd taken me to.

At this point I couldn't yet fly, but I could leap about and run like an Olympic athlete (at least that's what my mom said). She was always surprised at how far I could jump. She was also always in a panic when she was cooking and I took an interest in what she was doing, as I enjoyed bouncing around, unconcerned with the presence of a hot stove or oven. I was more of a risk-taker than my mom liked. I also didn't know any better. Stoves and ovens didn't exist in the garden. But my mom informed me early on in our relationship that stoves and ovens were dangerous, and that a run-in with either would've ended my life quickly. So, I kept what I thought was a good distance from both.

12

A Place to Perch

The hydrangea branch I arrived on didn't last very long. When it wilted and died, it forced me to find a new place to perch. My mom and dad fixed that quickly, creating a special new place in the kitchen window just for me. They cut a plastic bottle in half, filled the base of it with some rocks and water, and wedged some bamboo branches in between the rocks. They placed their creation on the wooden windowsill, the tops of the bamboo meeting up with the bamboo curtain that hung over the window, ensuring I would have easy access to crawl on the curtain if I wanted to. Plus, I'd have an unobstructed view of the garden below.

I liked the bamboo stalks themselves. They were excellent for perching. But I didn't like the leaves. They were flimsy and barely held me up, even when I was still tiny and practically weightless. But the leaves were the same color as I was, so they were excellent for those times when I wanted to play hide and seek.

me and some
of my perches

13
My Home, My Adventure

My mom had to tell me the names of everything in our cave, because every single bit of it (aside from the bamboo) was foreign to me. That's how I learned that, 1. My cave was apparently very small compared to many of the other caves in the neighborhood, and 2. The cave was made up of three sections—a combined kitchen and living room, a bedroom, and a bathroom. I spent most of my time in the kitchen/living room area, which is also where my mom spent most of her time when she was home. Sometimes she even slept there, on something she called the couch.

She called many of the strangely shaped items around the cave "fern itcher." I had seen ferns before in the garden, but I'd never heard of itcher ferns. These didn't look like any ferns I knew of either. They didn't even have leaves. They were more like oddly shaped stumps. The only purpose they seemed to serve was as a perch for humans.

The top part of our cave was called a ceiling (though from outside, it was called a roof, which I found confusing—why did the same thing have two names?). And the bottom of the cave was called a floor. Our floor was covered with something called a rug.

I liked to explore the cave, but without wings or my mom's help, I was extremely limited. Though I could climb everywhere, getting from one room to the other was a little more challenging.

When I first arrived, I was less than an inch long. Though I could jump five times my body length in a single bound, getting from the kitchen counter to bedroom door would've still taken me a few days if I had to rely solely on leaping. And I would've had to navigate the fuzzy rug on the ground (which I hated because my feet always got caught in it).

Anytime my mom noticed me on the move, she would pick me up and carry me over to the window ledge next to the couch. This particular ledge was always much warmer than the one by the kitchen window. (Though the kitchen window had a very pretty view of the garden's flowers, it didn't get a lot of sunlight.) The window next to the couch still provided a view of the garden, but I didn't care as much for the view it gave me as for the sunshine it let in.

My mom set up a small log on that windowsill, giving me another place to perch and climb. I happily sat on that log for hours, warming myself in the sun's rays. I had been warned by my mom that winters where we lived were cold and rainy, so I had a feeling I'd be spending a lot more time on the log in the months to come.

My mom also said that in winter, our cave was not only cold but very damp. Even the walls would get wet, which would make it difficult for me to climb on them. I appreciated the little log my mom gave me, as it was one of the few things that didn't get slippery. It was covered in lots of rough bark, perfect as footholds for a mountaineering mantis like me.

Sometimes, I would just sit on the window curtain. And sometimes I would attempt to hang out on the wall, though I'm not sure why I bothered. The wall, even when it wasn't damp, was very smooth, so it didn't have much for me to grip. I would fall off the wall every single time I tried to climb it. But that never stopped me from trying. I liked a challenge.

14

The Great Outdoors

For a short time, my mom took me out into the garden every few days because she seemed to think I needed "fresh air." After a few weeks of living in the cave, though, I was now thoroughly terrified of the outdoors. I liked the safety of my cave, with its very solid ceiling, walls, windows, and floor. It was like a fortress to me. Nothing bad could get in and get me. But in the garden, I was so exposed, and there were hundreds of things that could—and would—make a meal out of me.

My fear didn't stop my mom from bringing me outside, though, mostly because at first, she had no idea how terrified I was. I mean, how would she? I came from the garden. That was my birthplace. I would like to return to the garden, right? Makes sense. It just wasn't true.

The routine was this: she would put me down in the long grass, either sit or stand next to me, and wait for me to… what? Run around? Prance about in the grass? Leap from blade to blade? To be honest, I have no idea what she expected me to do. But I knew what I wanted to do, and it was not flitting about in the vast expanse of a very exposed lawn. I just wanted to get back to my perch in the window. INSIDE the cave.

She, being very protective of me, never moved too far away from where she put me down in the grass. And I would sit there in the same spot where she placed me, frozen.

My mom (who wasn't afraid of birds or lizards or really anything, come to think of it) was initially confused by my lack of interest in the garden. She assumed that I would love being back there. I was a wild insect. Why wouldn't I want to play in the grass? Why wouldn't I want to explore? After all, I loved exploring in the cave. But moving around outside meant I was a target. I was exposed. I might attract the attention of something terrible—something that might see me, swoop down, and take me away. And that would be the end of me. So, instead of exploring, I stood still as a statue. I was afraid to breathe. Not even my antennae wiggled.

It didn't take long for her to realize I wasn't enjoying myself. So, playtime in the garden would be over very quickly. She would put her hand down, and I would run back to the safety of her palm. Then she would take me back inside, shaking her head and giggling. I don't know why she was determined to get me outside. I guess maybe it's because I was the only wild animal she'd ever met who didn't like being in the wild. But she was stubborn, so we went out into the garden several more times before she finally gave up on the exercise.

One time she placed me on the garden fountain, which was dry at the time. She pointed something she called a camera at me and started pushing down on a button and making a clicking sound. Or the camera made the clicking sound. I'm not sure where the clicking came from, but it came from her general direction.

"We're doing a photo shoot. I'm taking photos of you," she said softly. "Today, you are a model." I had never done a photo shoot before. I didn't even know what one was. The whole process made zero sense to me, but honestly, I didn't give it much thought at the time because my mind was preoccupied with the possibility of danger all around me.

She placed me at the bottom of the stone basin, and I ran into the first shadow I could find. She frowned. It was too dark where I was, and she said she couldn't get a proper photo. She needed me in the light.

I finally relented after a few minutes of her coaxing. Ever so slowly and cautiously, I made my way out of the shadows and up to the top of the fountain, which had a little spire where I could perch. I put on my best brave face, knowing full well I was now in plain view of every feathered creature imaginable. She then took some of these so-called photos.

Overall, it was a terrifying experience, especially when a shadow crossed in front of the sun and I looked up to see one of those feathered fellows flying overhead and eyeing me. My mom, also perceptive enough to see the bird, quickly shuffled me onto her hand, hid me from view, and brought me back to the safety of the cave.

All but one of the other photo shoots we did from then on were done inside the cave. And she finally stopped trying to rewild me.

my modeling days

15

Dinner Is Served

I was an eating machine, especially when I was younger. We mantises grow quickly, so we need all the food we can get. While I was still growing, I had to eat every day, and I would even eat food the same size as me.

Though my dad caught me plenty of food when he was in town, it was my mom who did most of the "hunting" for me. She would bring dozens of crickets in from the garden and put them in a container she made from an old box. She punched lots of little holes through the sides of the box to allow air to get in and would put some water and food inside it for the crickets. When it was time for me to eat, she would take a cricket and place it in a spot in front of me, where it was sure to catch my attention.

Sometimes she would catch a fly, and, holding it with a pair of something she called tweezers, put it in front of my face until I grabbed it. More rarely, she would find a spider and place that before me. But always a small spider. A big one could've turned around and eaten me, so she avoided those.

DID YOU KNOW?
Mantises grow very quickly, so they have to eat every day when they are young. Sometimes they even eat food that is the same size as they are.

When local cricket supplies dwindled, she had to start foraging further afield. She would grab a smaller container and take walks down to the end of the road, where she said there was a very woodsy pathway filled with crickets, grasshoppers, and other mantises. She would catch as many critters as she could manage, put them in the tiny container, come home, and transfer them to the larger container. From that collection of unlucky insects would come my breakfast, lunch, and dinner.

She always apologized to each insect she took out to feed me.

Eventually, I would not need to eat every day. But regardless, feeding me was always a challenge. My mom was busy with something she called a full-time job, so she couldn't be running around searching for and catching insects for me day and night. And she kept a very clean cave, so there weren't really any around for me to catch myself. Winter was coming to Constantia, which also meant that, even in the garden, bugs would soon be in short supply. She needed to come up with a plan for feeding me once the bug supply ran out.

I was a messy eater

16

Grapes and Other
Culinary Curiosities

As the seasons began to change and my mom got very busy with work, it got more and more difficult to find live food. My mom started to get desperate. She rummaged through the fridge and the cupboards to see what she could feed me in place of insects that would still fulfill my dietary needs. One day, out of sheer frustration and after picking up and putting down a few items, she grabbed a small round green object, cut it in half, and placed it before me on the windowsill. She waited.

I had never seen a green thing like this before, so I wasn't sure what to do at first.

"It's a grape," my mom said. "Try it."

After a few seconds of no reaction from me, she gently pushed this grape thing closer and closer until it was practically under my mouth. I touched it with one leg, then lowered my face and took a small bite. And then another. And another. And another.

Very soon my entire head was submerged in the grape, and I was eating away. It was the tastiest thing I'd ever eaten. Where had grapes been all my life? Why had no one ever told me they existed?

My mom let out a sigh and smiled. She said she knew a grape wasn't the best option for a carnivore like me because it was mostly sugar, but it was a way to give me nutrients and calories and would have to do as a snack between protein-filled bugs. I didn't care to know what sugar was or why I shouldn't eat it. I just knew it was delicious. And I wanted more of it.

From that point on, I no longer ate only bugs and spiders. I expanded my palate and, after the introduction of the grape, got to taste all kinds of delicious things.

My mom had succeeded in transforming a carnivore into an omnivore.

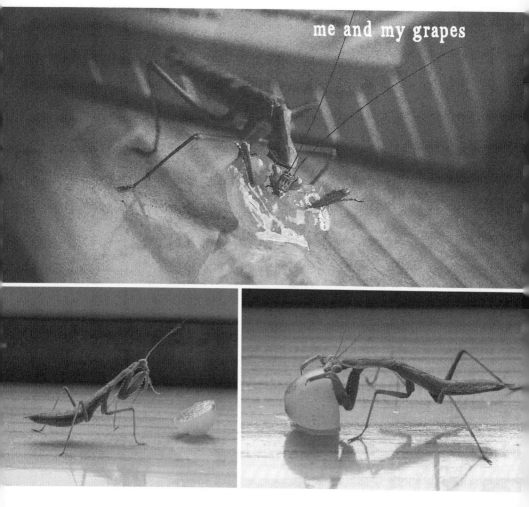

me and my grapes

17

Dietary Preferences

Though I loved grapes, mango was by far my favorite fruit. I will never forget the day she gave me mango. I was sitting on the window ledge, making faces at the birds outside, and she gently put a small piece of mango down in front of me. I wasn't sure about it—it was orange, not green like my precious grapes. But I decided to try it anyway and took a small bite.

Oh, the joy!

Within seconds, I had mango juice dripping down my forearms and face. Orange bits of mango stuck to my mouthparts. Even my antennae were covered in the stringy, orange-y goo.

As soon as I finished what she gave me, I immediately looked around for more. Must have more mango!!! She cut me another piece, and she didn't even have to put it down for me; I took it directly from between her fingers. And chowed down on the mushy sweetness. So much nom, nom, nom.

While I was busy eating, she was busy taking photos, shocked that a praying mantis not only ate grapes but also mangos. And loved them both!

She very kindly found me a wet cloth and gently cleaned my face when I was all done. I cleaned my legs and antennae myself. Mantises do something called threading, where we wipe our legs and antennae through our mouthpieces to clean off any food or debris. I always did it after I ate, and I often did it after an episode of falling behind the couch. My mom called this threading "mantis yoga." I called it being hygienic. I was very proud of being clean and tidy.

I got another mouthful of mango goodness when I did my leg threading that evening.

After mango, she thought it might be time to try some protein, so she boiled an egg and gave me a small piece of the white part. I knew what an egg was because I'd seen the ones in the nests of the birds in the garden. But I'd never eaten one. I didn't even know you COULD eat an egg. That did not stop me from tasting it, though. And once I got a mouthful, I proceeded to chow down. The piece of egg was gone in seconds.

Then she introduced me to boiled chicken. And fish.

I didn't even bother to wait for her to put the food down anymore; I just started taking it directly from her fingers all the time. I didn't snatch it from her, mind you. My mom taught me something she called table manners. She told me that I was not competing for food anymore, so snatching was not allowed. I would only get the food if I very gently and carefully took from her fingers whatever she was offering me. I was okay with that. I mean, the food wasn't going anywhere. I didn't really need to snatch it anyway because I didn't need to worry about the food running away. So, there I was, a praying mantis with table manners.

As far as food was concerned, it was all human food from then on. I didn't care if I never ate another insect for the rest of my days. I didn't want bugs anymore. I wanted eggs, chicken, fish, grapes, and mango. It appears my culinary tastes were a little more refined than your everyday mantis.

I'm not sure if my mom was relieved she no longer had to hunt down my meals or stressed that she now had to provide me with cooked meals. And she was doubtful about whether it was healthy for me to eat any of the foods she was feeding me. She was convinced that if a praying mantis could get clogged arteries, I would. I didn't know what an artery was. I didn't even know if I had arteries to clog, and I didn't care. I was thrilled about my new diet.

Though she gave me sweets, she never failed to provide me with something savory as well. And if there hadn't been proof in the way of witnesses or photos, I don't think anyone would believe some of the things she fed me. Steak (which I didn't like so much—it had too many stringy bits and was too hard to chew), bran muffins (which I DID like a LOT, especially the batter), nectarines, oranges, cream cheese icing (another favorite)… If it was in the cave, she offered me a taste. One time she gave me something she called cookie dough, which she made out of overripe banana, oats, and brown sugar. I ate it right off the fork.

I didn't like apples or any vegetables. No potatoes or other starchy foods (except the oats in the cookie batter, and bran muffins in all forms). Pork, like steak, was too stringy and I didn't like it. I didn't care, though. I loved the rest of my options.

I would especially look forward to nights when she made fish, especially when she fried it. Fried hake, fried tilapia, any fried fish—so delicious! And when she went out to eat, she would always bring me back a tiny bit of whatever she ordered to see if I approved of it or not.

No one believed her at first when she told them about my dietary delights. They thought she was making it up. Who feeds a bug fish? Or mango? Or cream cheese icing? And they were even less inclined to believe that she didn't just feed it to me. I would take it very gently from her fingers. But she had pictures to prove it.

I thought they were very rude not to believe her. Why couldn't mantises learn manners or have good taste? I certainly did!

I would sit on her hand and contentedly eat my meals, noshing away in the warmth of her palm. I think people thought she was crazy. I didn't. I thought my mom was amazing. And as far as I was concerned, she was the best mom in the world.

mealtime in our household

18
Water!

Like all living things, mantises also need water. We need it to stay hydrated, and we also need it to help us shed. Unlike humans, who just grow, and their skin grows with them, mantises have that hard exoskeleton that eventually gets too small for them, so they shed it and grow a new one. The process is called molting. And it is when I am most vulnerable, as my exoskeleton needs 24 hours to harden after each shed.

I imagine molting is an odd experience for anyone who doesn't have to go through it. And I will admit, my first molt was scary because I wasn't quite sure what was happening. Nobody warned me about this process. All I knew was that everything was fine, and then suddenly I hit a patch of a few days when it was getting harder and harder for me to breathe and move around. Then, just when I started to worry I was going to suffocate, BOOM! My exoskeleton split open, and the new, slightly larger version of me wriggled out of it. Santiago 2.0.

Now, every time I started to feel the pinch, I knew a molt was not far behind.

DID YOU KNOW?

As praying mantises grow, they shed their exoskeleton and grow a new one to accommodate their larger size. This process is called "molting."

I'm sure it looked a little weird for my mom to see the empty exoskeleton of a praying mantis sitting on the counter every now and again. In fact, the first time it happened she got a big fright, thinking I had died overnight. She walked into the kitchen, started to say good morning, and then gasped when she saw the remains of my old exoskeleton sitting on the counter. Seeing her panic, I wiggled my antennae to try and get her attention. Luckily, she saw them—and me. I was alive and well. In fact, I was more than well. Shedding meant that I was healthy and growing up. It was a good thing. Each time I shed my "suit of armor," it meant I was growing bigger.

And that's why water is so important for us. If we arthropods can't shed properly, we risk getting stuck in our old shell and dying. Water helps to keep our body moist so that we can more easily wriggle our way out of our old exoskeleton and grow a newer, bigger one.

Eventually, I would stop growing and shed for the last time, and that's when my wings would emerge. What a day that would be! I would finally be able to fly, though I'm not sure where I'd go. I didn't need to evade any predators in the cave. But still, to have the option to be able to fly was exciting!

To keep me hydrated, my mom would spray me every morning with a water bottle, ensuring I got sufficiently doused in water. I wasn't thrilled about that and was always trying to escape the spray, but I did like to suck the water droplets off my legs afterward.

When the cold set in, my mom would wipe the condensation on the windows with a towel, which created these little balls of water droplets on the glass. Then she would carry me to the window and let me sit on her hand and drink the condensation. That was my favorite way to drink. I loved how the sparkling bubbles of water just disappeared into my mouth. One minute they were there, the next... zoop, gone!

Eventually, she started to give me water from this weird tube thing she called an eyedropper. At first, I was afraid of it, but eventually I grew to like it because I could drink directly from the dropper and didn't have to get soaked every day. The dropper was much better than the spray bottle.

One time she tried to bathe me. She filled a bowl with a shallow layer of warm water and dropped me in. I immediately started splashing and flailing, trying desperately to escape. My mom, quick to react, removed me from the water as soon as she saw me struggling. She put my flailing body down on a towel, where she ever so delicately did her best to dry me off with a tissue. That was the last bath I got. Thankfully.

getting a sip of water from mom

19
Poop

Yes, I pooped. And I peed. Mantises have digestive systems and anuses, just like humans do. And everything that goes in up front comes back out the other end later.

My poop looked like little brown pellets, kind of like pepper corns, but smaller. My pee looked like water. It's not really all that exciting, to be honest. It's just a miniature version of what I assume human poop and pee looks like. Though I never actually checked or asked, now that I think of it. My mom and dad never pooped or peed in front of me. The humans I knew went to a special location for the event.

Not us mantises. We let loose whenever Nature calls. Which can be a bad thing, as you'll find out later in my story. Either way, I left little brown dots and tiny wet puddles behind whenever and wherever I felt the urge. My mom simply wiped it all up and put it in the garbage bin.

I pooped and peed on my mom's hand a few times, which I'm guessing she wasn't pleased about. But parents being

||||||||||||||||||||||||||||||||||||||||||||||||
DID YOU KNOW?
Praying mantis poop looks like little peppercorns and their pee looks just like clear water.

parents, they don't complain about that stuff. My mom just washed her hands and kept doing whatever she was doing at the time.

I did not fart. My dad did, though. He was proud of his farts. He was particularly pleased with himself when he ripped an abnormally loud or smelly (or both) "brrrrrp" from his butt.

I'm not sure if my mom was horrified or entertained or both, by my dad's appreciation of his own anal wind machine. She would giggle when it happened while simultaneously wearing a revolted look on her face.

I'm guessing she may have farted too, but my super-sensitive antennae never detected any farts coming from her. If she did fart around me, she managed to do so silently and odorlessly.

20

The Way I Saw Things

Mantises sway, but that has nothing to do with our shedding. We are the only insects with stereoscopic vision, which means we can see in three dimensions like humans.

Mantises have very complex eyes. We have two big ones on either side of our head. These eyes help us see movement and judge distances, and they are known as compound eyes. Flies and spiders also have these. Mantis compound eyes appear to have a pupil in them, which is called a pseudopupil. It isn't really a pupil; it just looks like one. It's more like a shadow that results from the way the light reflects on the eye itself.

Compound eyes mean we have lots of mini-eyes within each of those individual bigger eyes, and this allows us to have a greater range of vision. In fact, we can detect movement up to 60 feet away, or so I learned while watching a nature documentary about me. Well, not about me, exactly. About mantises in general. But hey, 60 feet! Not bad for such a tiny animal.

Most people think we only have those two big eyes, but we have five eye parts. There are three smaller eyes situated between those two big ones, wedged in the space of what you might call our forehead. These smaller eyes help with detecting light.

We often move from side to side to help us get a sense of how far away something is. It helps us with depth perception. Swaying also helps us figure out whether that's a bird circling above, or how far that chair is that we'd like to leap onto. It is a vital part of how we see. As you can imagine, I was a swaying machine when I first moved into the cave and had to learn my way around. Learning distances was crucial for my survival—since I didn't have wings yet, if I jumped and missed, I would land on the ground and might not be able to get up fast enough before someone stepped on me.

|||||||||||||||||||||||||||||||||||||||||||||||||||

DID YOU KNOW?
Praying mantises have "compound" eyes, meaning they have many tiny eyes that make up each one of their two large eyes. They can detect movement up to 60 feet away. They have three smaller "simple" eyes right between their antennae too. These simple eyes help the mantis tell dark from light.

Swaying isn't just to help us with our vision, though. We also sway when we are hunting. When we sway, we resemble a leaf or a stick blowing in the breeze. This makes us seem non-threatening to our potential prey and allows us to get within striking distance without being discovered.

When I hunted my food, I would sway for minutes at a time, slowly moving closer and closer to whatever prey was in front of me and making sure I was never detected. My mom tried to take a video of me stalking a cricket one day and finally gave up when she realized that in a full five minutes I had moved a grand total of an inch. I still had a few inches between myself and the cricket on the lunch menu. My mom did a quick calculation and realized she wouldn't be able to hold the camera still any longer without getting a cramp in her hand. She gave up with the camera.

Mantises are patient. Humans, it seems, not so much.

21

Shake It Up

Occasionally, my mom would find me shaking, which she at first incorrectly assumed was part of my process for stalking prey. She, not seeing any food around, wasn't quite sure what I was doing, so she used to say I was dancing, and she'd dance with me. I would wiggle; she would wiggle.

There was a good reason for the shaking, though, and it wasn't just for showing off my dance moves. Before each molt, I would shake to help loosen my old exoskeleton shell so that when I shed it was easier for me to shake the old shell off. However, I should've stopped shaking once I had my final molt, but I never did. I liked dancing with my mom, so I just kept it up.

My mom called my move the Santiago Shake. The name stuck. She would wiggle her butt, and I would wiggle mine. Even my dad would wiggle his butt when he saw me. It was like our family's secret handshake. Except, you know, it was a butt wiggle.

One would never call us an ordinary family. But if you ask me, ordinary seems kinda boring. Why be ordinary when you can be extraordinary? Different is so much more fun!

22

Danger! Danger!

There were plenty of danger zones in the cave, danger zones very foreign to the ones I would've learned about had I grown up in the garden instead of in the cave. Behind the couch was one such danger zone. And, despite the brilliant natural engineering of my feet, which were covered with fine little spikes perfect for gripping (except, apparently, when it came to damp cave walls), I fell. A lot. Especially behind the couch.

When my mom couldn't find me anywhere else, she'd head to the couch and look behind it and down into the darkness. And there I'd be, wedged between the couch and the wall, covered in dust and frozen in fear. She would fish me out and use a pair of tweezers to gently pull off the pieces of debris and fluff from my body, always careful not to touch my eyes. I would always clean my eyes myself.

I hated that space behind the couch. It was full of dust bunnies and shadows and who knows what else. If I got stuck there and my mom wasn't home, I might never come back out.

I liked to climb up the wall to these wooden things my mom called shelves and cupboards, which hung above the kitchen counter and where I would occasionally disappear for a day or so. My mom did not like that I liked the cupboards, though. When I ventured into their many crevices, I caused alarm bells to go off in her head. She, unable to see me in the dark spaces, would worry that I got stuck somewhere, was eaten by something, or fell behind the stove without her seeing me and was now being baked to a crisp while she was cooking dinner. All legitimate concerns on her part.

To keep up with me, she got very good at climbing herself, though I was significantly more graceful at climbing than she was. But that didn't seem to matter to her. Anytime I headed in the direction of the cupboards, she would immediately follow, clamber up on the countertops, fish me out from wherever I was hiding, and move me a safe distance away (and usually pointed in the opposite direction of the danger zone).

Another danger was the kitchen stove. If the stove was on and I landed on it (or in anything cooking on top of it), I would be toasted. Literally. Bye bye, mantis. My mom always made a point to keep me away from the stove when she was cooking.

Yet another danger was the cave-keeper.

The cave-keeper was a nice lady, and she always said hello to me when she arrived at the cave. But her job was to basically rid the cave of things like me, so my mom had to explain to her that I was not to be swept out, squashed, swatted, or vacuumed up. I was terrified of the vacuum. I saw how it swallowed up everything it encountered. I made sure I was far out of reach when that thing showed up and started shrieking away.

I liked to watch the cave-keeper as she swept and dusted her way around the cave. I'd perch on this weird thing that hung from the ceiling over the kitchen and looked like a baby sun. My mom said it was called a light. The light had a little edge around it I liked to perch on. There were other lights around the cave, but this one was the only one that hung from the ceiling, which is why I liked it. I could watch over everything from up high.

The kitchen was only a small area in the cave, so when I perched on the light, I was, unfortunately, also dangerously close to the stove. But I was careful, only ever poking my little head over the edge of it so I could see what was happening below.

My mom didn't like me on the light and would often crawl up on the cabinets beneath me so she could reach up and grab me and get me down from it. She preferred I stayed in other places when the cave-keeper visited, just in case. In fact, she began to make it a point to hide me under a curtain or place me on my perch by the couch window whenever the cave-keeper was about. My mom was desperate to reduce the likelihood that I might wind up stuck to the bottom of someone's shoe or thrown out with the trash, so if she could reach me to move me out of harm's way, she would.

Another threat was the wall heater. The heater was a large square piece of hard material that hung on the wall and was supposed to help heat up the bedroom. It failed miserably at its job. But though it failed to heat the room, it still managed to get incredibly hot itself. Hot enough, in fact, to burn my mom's hand when she accidentally touched it once, which caused her to let out an earsplitting noise that made me jump several inches high. It was the first and only time I'd ever heard her make a noise like that, and I was glad I only ever heard it that one time. It was terrifying.

My mom didn't like the wall heater. She often yelled at it, possibly because it burned her, but more probably because it couldn't manage to do the only thing it was supposed to do. My mom disliked when things didn't work the way they were supposed to work.

The heater stuck out about a half inch from the wall, a gap dangerously large enough that I could easily fall into the space between the plate and the wall and burn up. I stayed FAAAAR away from the wall heater.

My mom made sure that when she finally moved me to the bedroom (which she had to do at night once winter came because it was the only room in the cave with any heat at all), she kept me well away from that heated panel of death.

My mom also had a portable heater that would blow hot air, but I didn't like to be around it. I didn't like the feeling of any wind or breeze blowing on me. Wind threw me off balance. And not only did it literally topple me, but it made everything around me move, which interfered with my ability to judge where dangers were. For that same reason, I didn't like that strange thing my mom used to dry her hair. Plus, mantises have no eyelids; I couldn't close my eyes to protect them. Instead, my eyes would get blasted with hot air and dust particles, making them feel all scratchy and dry. When the portable heater or the hair dryer came out, I went and hid in the curtains. As a general rule, I did not like heaters.

23

Other Assorted Nightmares Lurking About

Threats were not confined to inanimate objects and the cave-keeper, though. I also had to worry about other living inhabitants of the cave, which included geckos and rain spiders, both of which happily eat praying mantises. The roof of our cave wasn't particularly well sealed, and there were plenty of spaces for these crafty creatures to sneak in.

The geckos were small and tended to stay in the bedroom cupboards, where they built tiny hidden homes among my mom's stuff. For a while it seemed like every single time it rained, a bright green baby gecko emerged from a cupboard. However, the geckos preferred snuggling in the clothes to scampering around the apartment (and in several months, I only ever saw one adult outside the cupboards, though I did see a few babies), so the geckos weren't too much of a threat. The rain spiders, however, were.

Rain spiders are about the size of an adult human's palm. They are very hairy and move very quietly and give mantises like me nightmares. Usually, the rain spiders popped up and then immediately disappeared, never to be seen again. But there was one that stuck around for many months. It was sneaky and showed up in a different place every time it made an appearance, so you never really knew where it'd be on any given day. Luckily for me, it avoided the curtains and getting too close to my mom. I learned that many animals tend to stay away from humans, except mosquitoes. Mosquitoes LOVE humans. Humans do not return the love.

Even my mom, who liked just about every animal (except mosquitoes), didn't seem to like the rain spider very much. While they can pack a mean bite, rain spiders aren't venomous and are only dangerous to humans if the human happens to be allergic to them, which my mom was not. The spider wasn't a threat to her. That said, she didn't like it staring down from the ceiling directly over her bed. I couldn't blame her. I'd also hate to have that giant staring down at me as I tried to sleep.

Though the spider didn't often appear in person, it was always lurking like an evil spirit in the back of my mind.

When my grandfather and dad built me a small cave of my own, I admit I was a little relieved to have an enclosed place to go at night, out of reach of spiders and the cave-keeper.

My mini-cave was rectangular, about two feet high, a foot wide and a foot deep. It had walls made of wire mesh, and there was a wooden pillar at each corner to hold it all up. It had a wooden base, and on top was a wooden roof on a hinge that allowed it to open and close. When I was inside it, there was no way that spider was getting anywhere near me. But from inside I could safely see out and watch it wherever it went.

Even though I liked my little cave within a cave, I ended up never really using it when I was with my mom and dad. I felt safe with them. The spiders avoided them. And my parents always came to my rescue when I was in need. Plus, the freedom to wander wherever I wanted to go was just too great an attraction for me to stay in one place for long. I couldn't bear being stuck in that little cave when I could be out adventuring.

me on top of my
own mini-cave!

24

The Interloper

Aside from humans who killed bugs on purpose, the last, and probably most dangerous, threat to my life was other mantises. And there were many. Though my mom never allowed adult mantids in the cave, they often popped up outside the cave window, sometimes a little too close for comfort. One bold female came around often, testing the limits of how close she could get to me and eventually causing my mom to step in and take charge of the situation.

When we feel threatened, mantises do something called displaying. We spread our wings wide and rear up on our back legs, extending out our front legs as far as they will go and essentially making ourselves look as big as possible. I think we look very impressive and intimidating. Not everyone agrees, though; my mom laughed the first time she saw me do it. Good thing she wasn't the one I was trying to scare away, and that I have that tough exoskeleton and don't take too many things personally. But if insects took every slight personally that a human sent our way, we'd all walk around depressed and moping constantly. Except for ladybugs and butterflies. People seem to like them, so they'd probably be fine. I don't get that, though. What makes them special? They can't do anything the rest of us can't do. Some things in life just don't make sense, I've learned. And humans seem to be one of those things. Anyway, I've drifted from my original story... let's get back to displaying.

The first time I ever displayed was when that one nervy female mantis popped up. She caught me completely by surprise. One minute, I was happily staring out the window and watching some starlings fighting with each other; the next, another mantis was directly in front of me. I reeled back, spread my wings and forearms, and put on my fiercest battle face. I was ready to brawl.

DID YOU KNOW?

When a praying mantis feels threatened by a predator, they spread their wings wide and stand up on their rear legs to make them look bigger. This is called "displaying."

My mom didn't see the other mantis at first. She just saw me, fully displaying at what initially looked like my reflection in the kitchen window. It was only when she walked up to where I perched that she saw the other mantis, who was hanging upside down on the outside of the window I was on. The other mantis was staring at me and very clearly trying to figure out how to get inside to where I was.

My mom's protective instincts kicked in.

Knowing that the other mantis couldn't get to me (the window was closed) and therefore couldn't hurt me, but also realizing that I was terrified of this potentially threatening newcomer, my mom quickly scooped me up and moved me to the couch window. Then she opened the kitchen window and shooed the other mantis away.

Though the mantis flew away, she didn't fly far. She apparently liked what she saw and was determined to meet me. Who could blame her? I was rather handsome.

A few days later, while putting something in the car, my mom found the same female mantis sitting on the railing of the steps leading up to our cave. The mantis just sat there, casually perching, hoping my mom didn't notice her. But my mom knew who she was. You couldn't mistake this mantis. She was a bruiser, missing half of her right front leg. Her wings had plenty of scars from fights with other insects (and possibly birds and small mammals). She had grown up sparring with any threat (of which it looked like there had been many) nature threw her way. I did not ever want to meet her in some dark alley, should I ever be in a dark alley. Which was unlikely, but still.

As soon as my mom got to within a few feet of the female (my mom named her the Interloper), the Interloper panicked and flew away. But in her panic, the Interloper flew directly into my mom's car and knocked herself out cold.

My mom, feeling a little guilty about giving the mantis such a fright, went down to check and see if the Interloper was okay. She gently poked the mantis until she woke up, after which the Interloper immediately panicked again and ran up the closest branch she could find (which happened to be my mom's arm), her rough feet nipping my mom's skin every step of the way.

At that moment, my mom grasped how different I was from other mantises. For one, I looked nothing like this mantis. The Interloper was stout and bright green all over, while I was slender and more mottled brown and olive. Also, my whole manner was different from hers. This mantis was rock solid and rough, and her legs were so prickly that they hurt my mom's arm as she ran up it. I, on the other hand, was gentle and soft. I moved slowly. I did not pinch when I climbed on my mom's arm.

I was, my mom suddenly realized, domesticated.

My mom managed to calm the Interloper down enough to get the mantis to a bush. Ever the caretaker, my mom then scrounged up a cricket from the driveway and fed it to the traumatized female. The mantis, much more relaxed now that she was half-hidden in the bush, greedily took the cricket and settled in to eat. That was the last time we saw her. I occasionally wondered what happened to her, but I must admit, I was happy she was gone. Female mantises have a reputation for luring male mantises to them with promises of love and then eating the unsuspecting male mantises when they get too close.

the Interloper and I meet

25

Taunting the Garden Dwellers

Aside from the heater, the stove, the cave-keeper, the rain spider, and a few shy geckos, living in the cave meant I was usually in a safe zone. Though in the warmer months the cave windows were usually open, birds, other insects, and other potential predators that might like to eat me usually stayed outside, lest they face the wrath of my mom. I was free to wander as I pleased, though my mom often got concerned when I got too close to the crevices near the ceiling. There were slats in the roof where a mantis could get lost forever. As with the cupboards, whenever she saw me moving towards those danger zones, she immediately leaped into action, climbing up the counter like a monkey, gently picking me up, and relocating me to a safer spot.

As I grew older, I became less interested in the ceiling and more interested in sitting near the window, no matter what window it was. From the window, I could watch the goings-on in the garden, and there was never a lack of action for me to watch.

Dozens of different types of birds zoomed from tree to tree, flower to flower. Sunbirds, Cape white eyes, doves, cuckoos, and even a tiny owl lived in our garden. And so many insects! Some used to come visit me, looking at me from the other side of the window and wondering how they, too, could live in the cave. I told them it was a single-mantis residence, though, so no room for anyone else. A few tried to sneak in, but my mom always managed to find them and shoo them out. She was particularly vigilant about making sure other mantises didn't get in, especially that tough female.

A few times some of the neighboring bugs and birds flew into the window glass in their desperation to get inside. But I was the only lucky one to live in the cave, though before I showed up, there were a few birds living there. The birds, however, didn't last very long. They were rescues that my mom tried to rehabilitate and release back into the wild. Unfortunately, both were too badly injured and didn't make it.

I did meet one bird. It was a rock pigeon my parents named Pidgie. Not a very creative name on the part of my parents, but considering the bird only lived for a day with us, I don't think it mattered what its name was.

The bird had been hit by a car on our street, so my mom, ever trying to save the world, took it home and tried to nurse it back to health. Considering the poor thing could barely move, let alone fly, it didn't pose a threat to me. My mom also knew she could put me in my little wooden cave if necessary, at least until the bird healed and could be released back into the wild.

The bird never healed. In fact, it died in my mom's arms. And my mom cried. I couldn't understand why at first since she barely even knew Pidgie. And mantises aren't very good at the whole "caring for others" thing anyway. We love our personal space and alone time. But the more time I spent with her, the more I started to understand that my mom wanted nothing more than to help as many animals (and people, though she probably would never admit that) as she could. It didn't matter if she'd only just met Pidgie, or if she'd known Pidgie her entire life. A life was a life. And she wanted to save every one. But she couldn't. That made her sad.

I felt a little guilty because I didn't know how to help her. And, to be honest, I was secretly relieved that Pidgie didn't last. Birds are my enemy, even sick and injured ones. I preferred being the only other living animal in the cave (aside from my parents, of course). But I never told anyone that.

watching the outside world
from my hydrangea plant

26

Living the Good Life

I think maybe I got a little lazy living with my mom. After all, I didn't have to feed myself anymore and, aside from the dangers I mentioned, I didn't have to hide from any predators. I spent most of my time hanging around by the kitchen or the living room window, watching the garden from the safety of my new home.

I liked to look at myself in the window (though at first, my reflection scared me). I had never seen myself before. I thought I was looking at another mantis creeping up on me. But my mom, always there to calm me down in moments of confusion verging on panic, said it was only my reflection I was seeing. I was looking at me. What a strange concept that was. I was staring at myself staring at myself staring at myself, to infinity. I had to make myself stop thinking about it before my head started to hurt. I wasn't built to process things that complicated.

My mom said certain surfaces in the garden also had reflective qualities to them, such as puddles. But even though the garden had plenty of puddles, I had never seen my reflection in them. I couldn't risk hanging out near puddles. Lots of animals hung out near puddles to drink, which meant I was exposed to possible predators whenever I was near a water source like a puddle. I stayed far away from them.

In fact, in the garden, there was nothing that had a reflective surface that was safe for me. But there were lots of reflective things in the cave that were safe for me. Like the windows. And the mirror. My mom would take me to the mirror now and again so I could get a better look at myself. It was fascinating to see all my body parts from all these different angles. So many moving parts.

I thought I was a very handsome mantis. My mom said so as well. And she had excellent taste.

checking out my reflection

27

You've Got a Friend

Though I didn't realize it at first, I think my mom maybe needed me as much as I needed her. I could tell she was lonely. She didn't have children. She couldn't have pets because of something called a landlord. Her significant other (my dad) was on the other side of the country and gone for weeks on end. Her family and most of her friends were on the other side of the world. Many of her friends in Constantia had moved away. She said she often felt ignored and invisible. And she worried that she wasn't making any sort of positive impact on the world. She told me many times she thought she was failing at life. I didn't think it was possible to fail at life, but I couldn't tell her that because I couldn't speak. I could only sit and listen.

She needed a meaningful connection, an outlet for all the love she had stuffed inside her, and a purpose. I was all she had. So, I made a promise to myself to do what I could to be that outlet, to accept that love, and to give her a feeling of meaning. I could be her companion. I could be her buddy. I could be her purpose. And then, when the time came when we both had reached a point where we no longer needed to lean on each other, we would part ways.

I thought it was very selfless and brave of me to take on such a role. And even though I didn't know everything there was to know, I understood how important it was for all of us to feel like we mattered. Even in the garden, each life form had a role to play, whether it was bees and birds pollinating flowers, or trees giving oxygen and shade, or mantises keeping insect populations in check. I wanted to help my mom find hers. That would be my role.

Praying mantises usually travel a much less complicated path and never get attached to anything. We certainly aren't known to help others on purpose. I had no idea what I was doing.

But I knew when I was fulfilling my new role. I knew it every time my mom smiled at me, every time she picked me up and sat me in her palm and told me how special I was.

To my mom, I was one of the most entertaining creatures around. She was often laughing at me. But not in a mean way. She didn't make fun of me or tease me. She just found me funny for some reason. She called me a character. I have no idea what that meant, but I liked it, mostly because she said it. I admit it; I adored my mom.

My mom said she liked the way my head swerved whenever she spoke to me, as though I was listening to her. But I WAS listening to her. I just couldn't talk back to her. It was frustrating to have so much to say and no way to say it to her.

She was a wildlife photographer, and, given the number of photo shoots we did, I figured she liked to use me as her model and take photos of me. She said I was extremely photogenic. I didn't know what that meant, but it made her smile. That made me happy. If I could've, I would've smiled right along with her, but with my hard outer skeleton, I was incapable of smiling.

She wasn't a very social person by nature, and though she seemed to like her small group of friends, who stopped by to say hello now and then (and who were always courteous enough to say hello to me as well), she didn't leave the cave a lot. I learned that was also because she didn't have a lot of something called money, which she said you needed to be able to do a lot of things when you're a human. "Movies, concerts, dinners… they are all expensive," she said. I didn't know what movies and concerts were, but I knew what dinner was. I thought she was better off just hanging out with me, eating grapes. But I know I wasn't much in the way of a conversationalist. And she seemed to like to talk. At least she liked to talk to me.

My mom had a big smile and an even bigger heart. I mean, it must've been big, because she had a lot of room for a lot of love in it. She seemed to love every animal she encountered. Sometimes that made me a little jealous. But despite several other animals (and people) coming to visit the cave, I was the only one who got to stay permanently, so the jealousy only lasted for short periods of time.

On certain days, she volunteered at a place she called an animal shelter, which was nearby. She would go and walk the dogs nobody wanted. She explained that some people would leave their dogs there and never come get them again. I thought that was terribly sad. From what I knew of dogs (aside from the annoying golden retriever next door who never stopped barking), they seemed like nice animals. Even though they had a habit of peeing on everything, including plants where mantises might be sleeping.

But she also told me a good thing about the dogs she worked with—sometimes new people came and adopted those abandoned dogs, giving them what she called a second lease on life. I didn't know what a lease on life meant. I didn't even know what a lease was. She tried to explain that it was a saying, a metaphor. I had no idea what a metaphor was, either. Terms that were not straightforward confused me. In the wild, animals need things to be clear immediately. There isn't any time to think about the meaning of something. Any animal that stops to daydream or think about anything deeply runs the risk of being eaten by something that doesn't bother to stop and ponder the meaning of life.

Regardless of my challenges understanding what my mom was talking about half the time, what mattered was that many of the dogs found new homes with new owners who would take good care of them. She never brought a dog home for us, though. She said she had always wanted a dog, but she didn't own our cave. The landlords did, and the landlords didn't allow pets of any kind. And dogs were considered pets. Plus, a dog might have eaten me. Even if only by mistake.

I was allowed to stay because of a loophole—the landlords didn't consider me a pet. And since I didn't live in a box or cage, I was pretty much just thought of as a normal cave resident. I briefly wondered if the landlords also had praying mantises living in their kitchen.

Anyway, instead of going out with friends, my mom often used any extra money for buying treats for these dogs she couldn't adopt. And for buying treats for me. Like cream cheese icing.

When I wasn't watching the drama in the garden, I watched my mom. She was not afraid to stand up for herself or me and didn't back down from a challenge. I liked that about her. She very firmly believed in fairness, but life was often not fair. Even I knew that.

On occasion, and when she got overly excited or cross, she seemed so intense that I wondered if sparks would fly out of her eyes. I think this intensity made it hard for her, as most people who came to the cave to visit seemed intimidated by her fiery personality. Even my dad was, at times. I know I was at first.

My mom's mom called her "the little bulldog." I thought that was fitting in some ways but not others. Though my mom was certainly tenacious, she wasn't as round as a bulldog. She didn't have all those wrinkles, either. And she didn't snore like they do. I know praying mantises aren't normally experts on bulldogs, but I knew a lot about them because of a nature documentary I watched with my mom. You can learn a lot from those things.

I found my mom to be warm and smart and silly and fear-less. But I'm not sure many other people saw that side of her. She tended to guard her feelings around everyone but my dad and me. I could tell because people would ask her how she was, and even though I knew she was angry or sad or frustrated, she would tell them she was fine. But she wasn't. I liked that I knew more about her than most people she knew did. I'm not sure if she liked that, though. I think she would've preferred more people to understand her. I get that. I knew how it felt to be misunderstood, or not understood at all. I would've liked more people to understand me as well. For whatever reason, many people don't like bugs. But very few of them get to know any of us. I wish they did. I think they'd like us more if they learned more about us and saw the amazing and valuable things we do.

My mom said I made her very happy, even though I wasn't cuddly, and she couldn't take me for walks and I didn't give her kisses. But that last part wasn't true. I DID give her kisses. They just weren't traditional kisses. I had no lips, so I had to improvise. I can understand why anyone would think I was incapable of kissing anything. But I did. I would rub my head against her palm and nuzzle her hand with my mouthparts. That was the best I could do. But I considered it a kiss, even if no one else did.

However, she was right on the other counts—I was not like a cuddly puppy, and she couldn't take me for walks (without fearing that I'd be swept away by some roving bird or strong breeze, of course). And I didn't like cuddling. At all. It made me feel like something was trying to attack me.

But I did like quietly sitting with her, even if it was just prop-ping myself on a pillow next to her and watching her while she worked or read. Her face was fascinating to me. It was like clay, scrunching up and stretching out in a million different ways. My face, hard as I tried, didn't do that, though I could turn my head 180 degrees, which no other insects can do. But I couldn't make my face look any different. I wore the same expression all the time—permanently alert and ready for action.

I also couldn't get my face to change color like my mom could with hers. Sometimes, after she'd been running around, her face turned very red. Occasionally, it went very pale, like during the moments when she thought she lost me. Or when she was sick. Mostly, it was a sort of very light brown color with olive undertones.

Now that I think of it, we matched, though she was several shades lighter than me and she wasn't mottled. But her eyes were. They were greenish-brown, with golden flecks that looked like tiny bits of sunlight. They changed color depending on the light and her mood, shifting from golden to cinnamon to olive to a combination of all three. She said her eyes were hazel. Which I guess meant I, with my brown and green body, was kind of hazel myself.

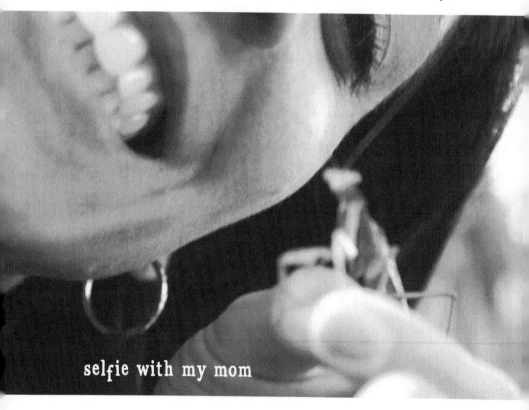

selfie with my mom

28

Understanding the Layers

My mom's body also changed color, but not the same way her face did. I mean, she didn't seem to change color the way, say, a chameleon does. A chameleon's whole body changes color. The skin on my mom's body stayed mainly the same color—a light tan. She just covered that skin with differently colored layers. Each day was some new color combination.

In winter, she often covered her legs in a blue, slightly rough layer, each leg like a little blue sapling sticking out from her abdomen. Sometimes the layer was black and smooth and followed the shape of her legs. Sometimes it was loose and sort of hung there like she'd wrapped a curtain around her midsection.

Her abdomen and arms were also covered completely in winter, in layers that came in various shades and patterns. Sometimes the layers were so thick, she looked a little like a cocoon, with nothing but a head and fingers poking out. During the coldest days, even her hands and head were covered.

I think all these layers were meant to keep her warm. It would make sense, then, that when summer rolled around and the temperature went up, the layers covered less of her body and weren't so thick. They were no less colorful, though. In fact, in summer, they were MORE colorful. She was like a walking bouquet. Sometimes the layers were green, sometimes blue, sometimes pink, sometimes red, sometimes white. Sometimes the layers even had weird patterns. I wanted to tell her that those patterns would never help her blend into the natural world, but I don't think that was the point of the layers. And she never seemed to care about whether she blended in, anyway.

Though I did find it a strange habit of hers to cover herself in layers, I also found it fun to see what layers she would put on each day. I even tried to predict what she'd cover herself in, though the only thing I ever got right was the blue layer she wore on her legs. She wore that layer a lot. She must've liked the color blue.

Personally, I preferred green. But nobody ever asked me. Which was fine because, well, I couldn't talk anyway.

My mom called the layers clothes. I preferred to call them layers. Just seemed like a better word to describe them. What was a clothes, anyway?

I might have liked to have had a layer or two of my own to put on, especially in winter. But I don't think anyone makes layers small enough for someone like me. Speaking of layers, since I had none of my own, I had nothing to keep me warm if the temperature dropped. Our cave had limited heat. Once winter set in, it was too cold to leave me in the kitchen at night. When evening fell, my mom would carry me to the bedroom, turn on the wall heater (though I don't know why, since it never worked), and place me on the long curtains. She would turn on a tiny floor heater, close the bedroom door, and disappear under a mountain of blankets.

I liked sleeping in the bedroom. It meant I could watch over my mom every night, perched above her like a small green and brown angel. I would nestle within the folds of the fabric, tucking myself in just enough to stay warm, but not too much as to obstruct my view of her. My little antennae always stuck out to help me sense danger. I knew I could not protect her from big things, but I could certainly help keep some of the small irritations away. Like flies. I'm sure flies serve a purpose. Everything does. In my mind, though, that purpose was food, not annoying my mom.

29

Finally Getting My Wings

When we are between 4-6 months old, mantises shed for the last time and sprout their wings. We have not one, but two sets of wings. One set is called the forewings. The second is called the hind wings. The forewings are tougher and act like an outer covering to protect the hind wings, which are more delicate.

I had been waiting patiently for the big day to arrive, and I knew I was getting close because in my last few sheds I had sprouted wing buds, little nubs that extended out ever so slightly on either side of my abdomen. Fully-fledged wings were not far behind.

Now, I have to say, we mantises don't get very excited about things. In fact, we pride ourselves on being very patient and calm and showing little to no emotion whatsoever. But no way was I being calm about my wings. For me, wings meant freedom. I wouldn't need to rely on my mom to get around anymore. How could I not be excited about the prospect of being able to cruise around the cave and investigate all these new areas I'd never seen, like behind the TV, which in

DID YOU KNOW?

Praying mantises get their wings after they molt for the last time.

my current situation was off limits? My mom said it was too dodgy back there, what with all the snake-like wires and dark spaces. Who knew what was hiding there, waiting to pounce on her naïve and unsuspecting mantis-child? I'm guessing the real reason was that she didn't like to clean that part of the cave (and the cave-keeper never did either), so maybe she was afraid I might get taken away by dust bunnies. I don't know. I still wanted to check it out.

My mom woke up one sunny morning to find me on my bamboo branch with four soft tendrils of featherlike appendages hanging from my body. My wings had finally started to pop out! But wings don't just appear fully formed. They sort of unfurl over the course of several hours, delicate at first and eventually hardening as the day goes on. Mine had only just begun to appear, so they were a bit awkward and small, four little leafy projections resembling dainty, pale-green gauze ribbons shooting out of my back.

My mom knew not to touch me at all during this time, as my wings were extremely fragile and even the slightest touch could warp them and make them unusable. She did continue to check on me periodically to see how I was doing and to watch my metamorphosis, though.

As the day went on, my wings slowly unfurled more and more, emerging like gossamer coattails. They were beautiful and sheer and had an intricate lacy patterning on them, and they made me feel like I was growing a superhero's cape. Yes! Super Santiago! Had a nice ring to it, I thought.

Though they looked very light, my wings were a lot heavier than I expected, and when I tried to walk across the windowsill, I found I could barely hold myself up. I made a mental note that I would need to start doing some more leg-strengthening exercises. Then I realized I didn't know a single one. How does a mantis strengthen his legs? Running up and down branches? Did I even have muscles? I MUST have muscles, right? My mom and I would need to do some research about mantis physiology once this wing thing had played itself out.

Luckily for me, as my wings started to harden, they also started to get lighter. Relief! Now I was just counting down the minutes until they were solid enough to try out.

The whole process took several hours, during which time the inevitable happened. Nature called.

I had to pee desperately.

In the process of relieving myself, I got one of my newly forming wings wet. The moisture made it curl up unnaturally. And no matter what I did, it would not uncurl. My wing! My beautiful wing!

My mom, seeing the mess I made, jumped into action. She found an earbud and delicately dabbed at the wet mess with the soft cotton, trying to gently soak up the liquid while being extremely careful not to touch the wing itself and cause any further damage. Though she did manage to sop up some of the pee, she couldn't get it all without further interfering with the wing development. There was nothing we could do but wait and see if the wing managed to flatten out on its own.

After a few more hours, my four wings solidified completely, shifting from the paper-thin light green tendrils I started out with to an almost stained-glass-looking solid column of mottled greens and browns (and pinks, surprisingly). I finally had wings. But what should've been my best day turned into my worst. That one hind wing never flattened out. It stayed slightly curled and caused a small ripple on my back when it was folded away. I was to be forever cursed with one wonky wing.

It wasn't the way it looked that bothered me. It was the fact that the dent prevented the wing from being aerodynamic. And that meant that I would never be able to fly properly.

I drooped like a deflated balloon. If I were capable of it, I probably would've cried. The big day for which I had been waiting for months had arrived, and I had ruined it because I simply couldn't hold it in any longer.

My mom said it was okay; she would always be there to carry me wherever I needed to go. But I was sad. I wanted to fly like the other mantises. And now I never would.

Wonky wings aside, now I was fully grown. I had an olive-green head, abdomen and legs; and bright grass-colored eyes. My wings were mottled brown, tan and olive green. The hindwings also had some pink in them. Along the inner side of each forearm was what looked like a faint bluish stripe along with two dark patches. And the insides of my mouthpieces were very pink.

At 3 ½ inches long, I was as big as I was ever going to get.

my wings arrive

30

Flying 101

Yes, my flying skills were flawed because of my rippled wing. That never stopped me from trying, though, and in my mind, I was nimble and impressive when I did try. But if you asked my mom or dad, dive-bombing, base-jumping, or parachuting are probably better descriptions of my technique than flying, more in the vein of a kamikaze pilot than a peregrine falcon. Soaring and cruising were not things I would ever be able to do on my own. However, I learned to improvise.

My one deformed wing meant I was unable to steer myself and hold myself alight properly, so I often fell short of where I was aiming. Sometimes I would bridge the gap by luck, usually because I was "flying" from a high place to a lower place, and gravity and physics just happened to work in my favor. Most times I would come crashing down, a green and brown blur of desperately flapping wings attempting to break the fall.

No one would ever call my flight attempts graceful.

When I was in the living room, I often tried to launch myself onto the couch from the wooden log I perched on in the windowsill. Though the distance was small (maybe 1 ½ feet), this was a scary endeavor because if I missed (and I missed more than I made it), I ended up behind the couch and in the dark realm of the dust bunnies. If my mom didn't find me immediately, I would be stuck there for hours, unable to get the layers and layers of dust off my body and navigate back up to the light.

Why so much fear about the dust bunnies? Dust bunnies are silent, terrifying, blob-like warriors who lay in ambush, using their excessive fuzziness to trap and kill their enemies. They are so skilled that they don't even need to move to do damage. An unwary insect just needs to stumble into one, and it's "Game Over" for the insect. The dust bunny's fuzz sticks to whatever it touches, eventually overpowering its prey by weighing it down and confusing it in a mass of fuzziness. The victim, enveloped in a scratchy gray cloud, can't find its way out of the darkness.

Most insects didn't survive encounters with dust bunnies, including mantises. I know because in the short moments I spent behind the couch, I saw the remains of some insects who'd faced them and lost the fight. It was a bug graveyard back there, filled with many dust-covered arthropods who did not have a mom like mine to save them. I wondered if my mom left the bodies there on purpose as a reminder to me to stay away.

As much as I feared dust bunnies, I had to admire them. Their tactics were so simple, yet incredibly effective. Lucky for me, I had an attentive mom who did not fear dust bunnies, and who rescued me from encounters with them and other potential mishaps on average twice a day. In fact, given my love for exploring and my thousands of attempts at flying, I'm not sure how she ever had time for anything BUT rescuing me. And feeding me. But moms, I've learned, are excellent multi-taskers. Somehow, she always managed.

31

Friends and Family and (Unfortunate) Guests

While I was the solo pet (if you could really call me a pet) in the cave, I wasn't alone with my mom. There were also three tiny stuffed animals—two otters and a monkey. Their names were Seaweed, Barnacle, and Cheeky, respectively, and they were the rest of my surrogate family. So, even though I was sad about my wings, I knew I was lucky in other ways: I had friends to cheer me up. And that was one of the many things that made my life special—I had friends. No other mantis in the world could say that. They all ate their potential buddies. I couldn't eat mine. I would've choked on them if I tried. They were stuffed with fluff and fuzz.

I often liked to crawl on Seaweed and Barnacle's heads because they had short fur, but Cheeky's fur was thick and fuzzy (like that awful rug), and it stuck to my feet. I stayed away from Cheeky. He didn't take it personally. Or at least I don't think he did. Like me, he couldn't talk, so I guess I would never know.

Because the stuffed animals didn't do much beyond sitting around, and because my mom didn't want me to be lonely, she was often bringing new "friends" into the house. I think she assumed that since she fed me so well, she wouldn't have to worry about me eating the company. I wish I could say it worked that way. But it didn't. Gringo, the grasshopper, lasted a day. And not by his choice. Fernando, the baby mantis, lasted a week. He probably lasted that long because my mom played with him a lot, so he was usually out of my reach. He was adorable. But he was also oblivious. And tasty.

The butterfly was an accident. My mom found it attached to the side of the cave entrance, trying to emerge from its cocoon. It got stuck in the process, and my mom stepped in to help pull it out. One wing wasn't uncurling, so she brought the butterfly inside and laid it out on the kitchen counter. Even though it wasn't her fault, nor did I blame her, I think she felt badly about my misshapen wing and took it upon herself to try to make sure this butterfly did not meet my same fate.

She was in the process of flattening the wing out when I, who had been watching the scene unfurl, slowly and stealthily made my way closer and closer to the injured animal. When I was close enough, and before my mom noticed me there and had time to react, I pounced on the butterfly. My mom, horrified, immediately tried to dislodge my forearms and free the poor insect. But once we mantises grab on, we do not let go. In a matter of seconds, my mouth was stuffed with orange butterfly wing.

The stick bug managed to escape before we were properly introduced, which was fine. It didn't seem to have much meat on it anyway.

me and my
stuffy family

some of the unfortunate guests

32

Juanita

Then there was Juanita.

My mom found Juanita in the grass along the pathway she took on one of her daily walks. Juanita was a nymph, only about an inch and a half long, and missing one of her back legs. Unlike me, who was bright green as a baby, Juanita was straw-colored, almost translucent. My mom, despite logic, the natural order of things, and multiple past experiences of me eating any friends she introduced to me, decided to bring her home.

Juanita was a very brave, adventurous little mantis. She never let her missing leg slow her down. In fact, she never seemed to stop moving, often climbing up and down the walls to inspect every single crevice and crack. She wasn't afraid of anything, including me. She would often crawl on my back, something that always set my mom on edge with worry as she wasn't quite sure how I would react. Would Juanita be the bug I finally befriended? Or would I succumb to my instinct and eat her?

For a good week, I tolerated Juanita, and we lived together peacefully. But one day I got fed up with her climbing on me. She was very clingy and had no concept of boundaries. I liked my space. I tried to tell her. I moved away from her. I shook her off. I swatted at her with my legs. She didn't take the cues.

My parents had gone out to run some errands, and when they returned, half of Juanita was missing. I was busy leg threading and had, my dad said, a suspicious look on my face. My mom's face and shoulders sagged as though someone dropped a heavy weight on her. She said my name very softly, and with such disgust and sadness and disappointment that I was depressed about it for the next week.

Even if my mom hadn't been upset with me, I probably would've still felt terrible about Juanita. Juanita was very nice. She might have accomplished great things. But I am a praying mantis, and this is what we do. That's why we are loners. And why giving us stuffed animals as companions is a better idea than trying to find us living friends.

Not surprisingly, I became very close with Seaweed, Barnacle, and Cheeky. They didn't care that I was quiet and reserved and preferred to be the only child. They accepted me for who I was and never asked any questions.

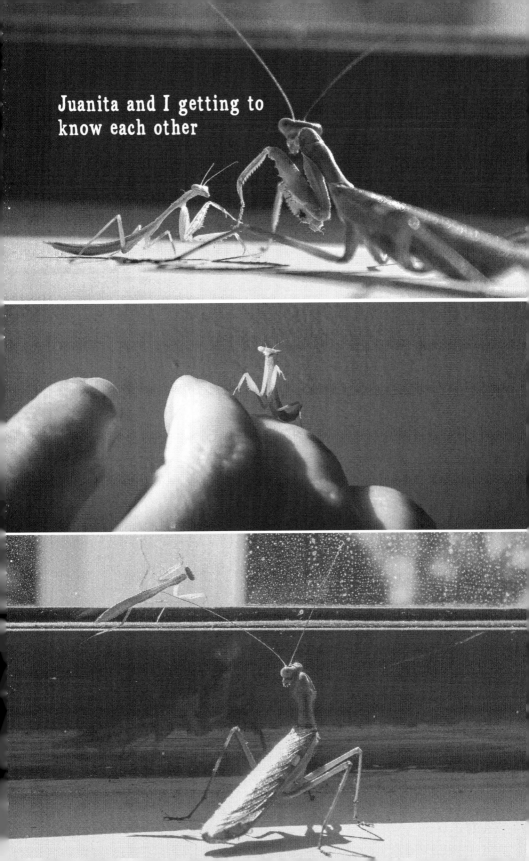

Juanita and I getting to know each other

33

Even Small Things Matter

Although many people told my parents we were an odd bunch living in unusual circumstances, my parents and I ignored the doubters and made the best of things. My mom, the stuffed animals, and I would sit down and watch nature documentaries together. Watching documentaries was my favorite activity because the shows taught me about people, places, and wildlife not only in my small world but on the other side of the world as well. They also taught me that I wasn't the only one who thought praying mantises were extraordinary creatures.

There are all kinds of folk tales about us. In both the Khoi and the San culture here in South Africa, Mantis (as he is known in the legend) is honored as a god and not just any god: a top god. In some African cultures, mantises are believed to bring the dead back to life. I'm not sure if that means we create zombies, but regardless, it's cool to think we can resurrect someone or something.

In Asia, mantises are considered good luck; we are celebrated and honored. In China, we are symbols of fearlessness, and there are two separate forms of martial arts fighting named after us (based on many of the smooth moves I performed naturally, by the way). In France, legend has it that a praying mantis will point a lost child home. In Arabic and Turkish cultures, mantises are believed to show the way to Mecca. I'm not sure what Mecca is, but I've been told it's a big deal for some people.

Mantises are often seen as symbols of good luck. And, not surprisingly, we are also symbols of patience.

We even have a lethal shrimp named after us! It's called a mantis shrimp, and it punches out its prey. If you don't believe me, look it up.

I was chuffed when I learned all of this. I knew that praying mantises were cool, but I was over the moon to hear that others saw how impressive we are as well.

One of the biggest lessons I learned from these documentaries (and from my mom) was that no matter what we look like—whether we have two legs or six, skin, feathers, or scales—we are important and have a specific and unique place in the world. All things, big and small, matter in life. And we are all connected to each other. She called this connection the web of life. I wasn't sure about that name. Reminded me too much of the rain spider.

Anyway, no matter how special we may be, when we are small, we must also be that much more careful. Especially (in my case) of chickens. Why chickens, you ask? Why would a mantis in my situation ever need to worry about chickens?

Well, let me tell you about Bun.

34

Mantis Sitters

Occasionally, my parents both had to be out of the cave for a few days. Rather than drag me along, they would send me to a mantis sitter, someone they trusted would take good care of me and keep me well-fed and safe. But one particular sitter had a chicken named Bun. And Bun was terrifying. She was unpredictable and territorial, with beady, shifty little eyes that kept their evil stare directed at me the whole time I was at her cave.

Bun never spoke to me, though she did strut around and make lots of high-pitched squawking sounds that seemed to indicate she was not happy with my being there. I think she was also an only child (or at least an only chicken) and she didn't like to share her space with those she didn't know and who took attention away from her.

I'm also certain she was trying to figure out how to make me her lunch.

My caretaker (her dad), seeing the potential deadly interaction that could occur between his domineering chicken and his friend's praying mantis, made sure I was always out of Bun's reach. Because of his thoughtful actions, Bun failed in her efforts to eat me. I returned home in one piece.

My human grandfather had a much less scary home to visit. He was very good with carpentry and made me my mini-cave I mentioned earlier. Though I didn't stay in my mini-cave much at home, I did stay in it when I visited my grandfather. To be honest, I wasn't given a choice in the matter, but I understand why. He was afraid if he let me wander about he might lose me and then have to answer to my mom, who would not be pleased if her mantis son disappeared on someone else's watch.

Also, he often took care of me while staying at his daughter's or his sister's cave, both of which were places filled with potential dangers such as the curious hands of little children or a blind dog that stumbled over everything in its pathway. My grandfather always felt he'd rather err on the side of safety than face my mom's wrath. I didn't blame him. For such a little person, my mom could be fierce (and fiercely protective). I'm convinced she could bring down the heavens if she wanted to do so.

Anyway, when I was with my grandfather, into the mini-cave I would go. My mom filled it with branches and leaves, and I could climb around day and night without any fear of being trampled by an unsuspecting human or dog. Aside from being eaten by another predator or facing dust bunnies, being stepped on was my next greatest fear. My parents always told me to stay off the floor, and whenever they found me there, they picked me up and put me back on a curtain or window or another high point. I didn't understand why the floor was so awful (except for the annoyingly scratchy rug), but then they told me about a terrible mantis accident they saw in a place called the Sabi Sands.

The mantis had been warned to stay off the floor because people walked through that particular area all the time and didn't always look down. The mantis didn't listen. He said he could just fly away if someone came too close. One day, his attentions were occupied by a few nesting sparrows, and he found himself on the bottom of someone's shoe. Yep, someone stepped on him by mistake. The end.

Nobody could blame the person who squooshed the mantis. The mantis was brown and blended in with the concrete. It's that whole camouflage thing. The person who stepped on him simply didn't see him.

I had nightmares for a week after hearing that story. Lesson learned.

By keeping me in my cave whenever I was with him, my grandfather made sure no one could step on me and the dust bunnies could not get me.

Just like when I was with my mom, I ate like a king with my grandfather. He fed me boiled eggs and other delicious things. He seemed very proud of me, telling stories about me to everyone he met, and he always checked in with my mom to let her know how I was doing when she and my dad were away.

He watched a lot of sport on television, particularly cricket, which I learned was not unusual for South African men. I didn't understand why anyone named a sport after something I ate. And I didn't quite understand why men liked to tackle each other or hit a little white ball, but I did envy the ball. I imagined what it must feel like to soar through the sky, weightless and free. Then again, they hit the ball with a big stick. I would NOT like to get hit with a stick, even if it sent me flying.

35

Mom Bonding

When my mom was home, we did a lot of activities together. Often, I would sit on her knee while she worked on what she called her laptop computer (which I didn't quite understand, as it was rarely actually on top of her lap). She explained what a laptop computer was and how it worked. She did this thing she called typing, where her fingers would dance around little black keys with symbols on them and create tiny scribbles on the laptop screen. I loved the tap-tapping of her fingers as they whizzed away on those keys. At night, the keys would even light up.

I wish I knew what the little symbols were that popped up on the screen as her fingers flew around the keyboard, but I never learned how to read. That's okay, though, because my mom would read to me, sharing the stories she wrote and telling me about my ancestors and relatives. She would often look up information on praying mantises on the internet, trying to figure out why I did certain things. I guess this is what humans do with their children. They learn about the different stages of development and what to expect at different ages. My biological mom would've never done that. She just assumed her children would all take care of themselves. Which we would, but still. It was nice that my human mom made such an effort to take good care of me.

My mom could be very soothing and was able to calm me down when I was stressed. One particularly terrifying moment comes to mind. We were watching a nature documentary on praying mantises, and I was enjoying learning more about my species and seeing the different variations of praying mantises around the world. That's how I found out about orchid mantises. Even though I thought they were a bit…showy, I had to admit they were beautiful.

While I was daydreaming about meeting an orchid mantis, a massive mantis about twenty times my size suddenly appeared on the screen in full display. Violently thrown out of my daydream, I panicked. I attacked the computer, rearing up on my back legs, extending my wings out as far as they would go, and attempting to take on the giant mantis in front of me. I head-butted the screen and then bolted behind the computer, peeking my head out and thrashing my arms and wings in the air. I was ready to face off with whatever came my way.

My mom immediately turned off the program. Giggling, she then gently coaxed me out from behind the computer. I don't know why she was laughing. It wasn't very funny. If I had a heart, I could've had a heart attack and died. But mantises don't have hearts, at least not like the ones humans do, so I didn't die of a heart attack.

After a few minutes of her talking very gently to me, telling me it was okay and I was safe, I calmed down, dropping my arms and outstretched wings. My mom started the documentary again, this time skipping over the giant mantis part, and I settled back down on top of the keyboard to watch.

Aside from watching movies and keeping her company while she worked, I also used to help her in the kitchen. She called me her sous chef, which she said meant I was her assistant. She would sit me on the bamboo blinds that hung on the kitchen window and talk to me about what she was cooking, explaining to me about ingredients and how to measure (which she rarely did). She didn't enjoy cooking, though. She said it wasn't much fun to cook for just one human, and with my dad gone the majority of the time, most days she was only cooking for one. Well, maybe one and a half, if you count me. But still.

There were many nights of fried hake, fried eggs, boiled eggs, boiled chicken... the list goes on and on. No matter what she was making for herself, she always made sure to make something for me (with minimal seasoning because she didn't know if my body would cope with seasonings like rosemary and garlic). I was content with plain food. I guess I didn't know the difference: to me, a chicken was a chicken was a chicken. Also, I'll selfishly admit that I got a strange satisfaction out of the idea of feasting on a relative of that nasty Bun.

Even though I didn't taste them all, I loved the smells from all the different foods she made. Yes, mantises can smell as well as hear and see and feel.

I'm sure the other mantises in the garden watched with envy as my mom fed me bits of fish and butternut.

There were some things about me that she never understood entirely, like why my eyes turned reddish at night. I didn't quite understand why that happened, either. My mom did some research and asked an entomologist (that's a scientist who studies bugs), and she learned that it had to do with light spectrums and how the eyes absorb and reflect light. She left it at that. To be honest, it was all way too complex for me to follow anyway. And all I cared about was that as soon as the sun came up, my eyes went back to being bright green again.

36

Games and
Miscommunications

Hide-and-seek was my favorite game, mostly because I was really good at it. I loved to hide in the folds of the curtains, with nothing but the tips of my antennae sticking out and waving around. However, not being able to talk meant I couldn't tell my mom I was playing. There were many mornings when she came into the kitchen, let out her usual "Good morning," and then panicked because she couldn't find me. With my natural hiding skills combined with my camouflage, I was really good at being difficult to find.

She would frantically search for me, first looking around her feet to make sure I wasn't about to be (or hadn't already been) stepped on. Then she would scan the ledges and many surfaces in the kitchen for any movement. Eventually, she'd gently lift and shift the leaves of my bamboo or uncurl the curtain until her eyes hit upon some part of my body. Usually, it was a twitch of my antennae that gave me away.

After a while, she'd trained her eyes so well that she could find me easily among the greenery and the folds. And I eventually found my favorite places and stuck close to them, which also made it much easier for her to locate me. But for a while,

I know my love for hiding caused a few breathless moments for her.

Once my mom figured out I was playing and where my favorite hiding places were, she would do her best to NOT find me right away, even though I was almost always hiding in the curtain folds. I wasn't very imaginative, I guess. But the curtains were the only possible hiding place in the cave that didn't scare me. They were safe. So, they were always my first choice. Well, they were pretty much my only choice once the bamboo died. But like I said, she played along anyway.

She would pretend she didn't know where I was, checking every crevice, under the bed, on top of the counters, behind the couch, even inside the cupboards. She would always leave the curtains for last. Then she would let out a big sigh and act all surprised when she finally "found" me.

One time, I crawled between the kitchen cabinet and the wall. My mom was in the middle of doing something and couldn't get to me in time to keep me from disappearing into the darkness. I easily slipped between the wall and the cabinet, but the space was too small for her hands. It was also deep, and I'd gone way in. She tried to wedge a flat, shiny thing into the gap and gently nudge me up and out. But I moved farther away from the opening and her.

She tried out a variety of potential mantis-saving objects, each one longer and skinnier than the last. But none were long enough to reach me.

After a few minutes, she let out a huff, stopped her attempts, and scrunched up her nose and mouth (she did that a lot when she was thinking). Then she left the room. She came back with a bent and wiry metal stick that looked a bit like my antennae—but much bigger and thicker—and then proceeded to reshape it into a long, thin rod. She slipped it into the space and managed to delicately push me out over the top and down the front side of the cabinet. I thought it was hilarious. She was not amused. She promptly picked me up and put me back on the bamboo. The next day she had wedged some white fluffy stuff into the crevice.

I'm pretty sure she was in crisis mode for most of my life because of episodes like this one, of which there were many. Given my love of exploration and the various places in the cave where I could easily disappear, I kept my mom constantly on high alert. She was such a good sport about it all, though, never getting mad at me for my exploring. I think she was a bit of an explorer herself. I mean, she did move to the other side of the world all alone, leaving her family and friends behind, to live in a tent in the middle of nowhere and work among wild animals, many of whom could've easily killed her. But she said she loved learning and doing. She understood my need to discover new things. That was one more reason I loved her.

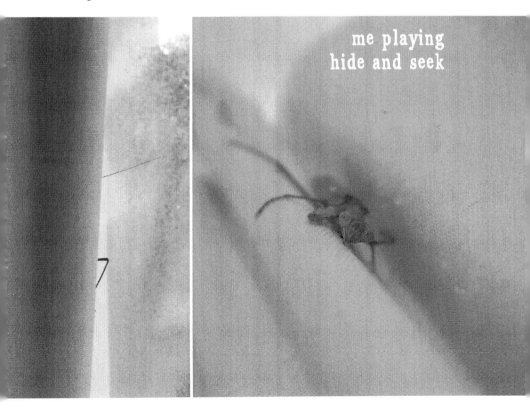

me playing hide and seek

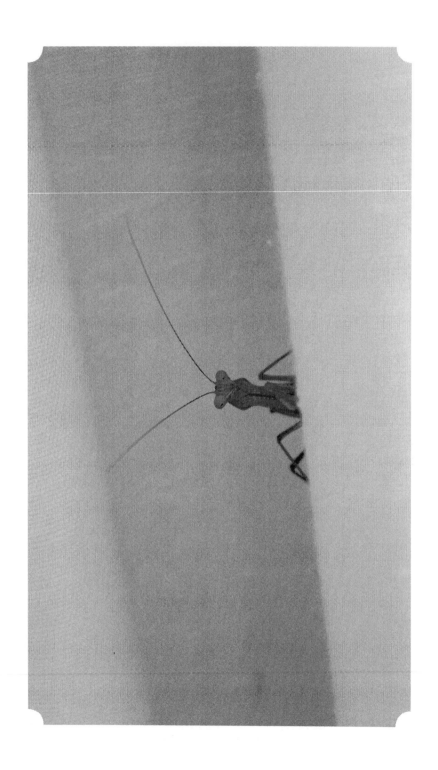

37

Easter Egg Hunt

Though I loved hide-and-seek, my favorite game by far
was the Easter egg hunt.

My dad was home on leave from his job, and my parents thought it would be fun if we all went into the garden one Sunday. I didn't know why this Sunday was any different from any other Sunday, nor did I care what "Sunday" meant, but this was a special Sunday, as on this Sunday they brought out something called Easter candy. It amounted to one shiny, rainbow-colored egg. I'd never seen an egg like this one. My mom said it was a chocolate egg. I didn't know what chocolate was, but I did know what an egg was, and I was very excited!

My mom placed the egg in the grass and gently lowered me down beside it. I wasn't sure what to do. Could I eat this glorious thing? I decided to investigate, climbing on and around the mysterious rainbow egg. Then I heard a click, and I quickly turned my head to see my mom with her camera, snapping away. I was confused. Why was she taking pictures of me and the rainbow egg?

After a few minutes, I think she could see my frustration, and she picked me up and took me inside. She took off the outside layer of the egg (the colorful part was a wrapper, she explained, and not something you eat), and placed the now brown egg in front of me. I moved closer to investigate once again. Then my mom took the egg away AGAIN and bit into it. What?!? This was MY egg. Why was she eating it?!?!?

She said that the egg's shell was made of chocolate, and chocolate is poisonous to a lot of animals. She didn't want to make me sick. I couldn't figure out why she would give me a chocolate egg to play with if I couldn't eat it, but as I said before, humans often fell into the category of "things in life that don't make much sense."

She did, however, give me a taste of the non-chocolate gooey inside, which was very sweet and delicious and got stuck in my mouthparts. I took a few nibbles and then sat back, very satisfied with my Easter egg experience. For the next hour, I threaded away all the sweet bits.

I was sad to learn that the Easter egg only appeared once a year, but that was okay. There were plenty of other delicious things my mom let me eat. One Easter egg was enough.

I'm still not sure why they called it an Easter egg hunt, as I didn't have to hunt for the egg, but if that's what they wanted to call our little adventure, that's what it would be called. And I guess it's better that the egg wasn't hidden. I doubt I would've found it otherwise. Not without becoming somebody's lunch in the process. My parents were clever; they wouldn't knowingly put me in harm's way.

my Easter egg hunt

38

A Picture Is Worth a Thousand Words

My mom was very involved with something called "conservation." She was a champion of saving animals and wild places. She did lots of writing and photography to help organizations working to protect animals and their homes. At first, I was confused by this. I didn't understand why everyone didn't automatically care for and protect the planet. I mean, everyone lives on this planet, enjoys its resources, and depends on it to survive. Shouldn't they, therefore, take care of it and protect it? I did my part. I ate pesky insects that caused damage to plants. But I learned that not everyone sees how we are all connected, and how the way we treat one species or ecosystem affects the other species and ecosystems.

The biggest problem my mom said she faced was that she met many people who didn't think they, as one single person, could make a difference. But that's not true. All of us can. Even if it's only a small one, it counts. My mom spent most of her time trying to show people that they mattered and that every one of their actions mattered as well. I have no idea if it helped or not, but I know she certainly put a lot of time and effort into it.

Not wanting to leave me out, my mom often included me in projects she worked on, such as a big one concerned with saving rhinos. She took photos of me alongside powerful messages about helping wildlife worldwide and getting people involved in protecting the planet. There was my face, on posters and in emails, a little green mantis of salvation. I felt like a superstar. Maybe I would even become famous. Maybe I would be Super Santiago after all!

Not all my pictures were used to help save wildlife, though. Some of our photo shoots were just for fun. My mom would place me on flowers and trees (and that horrible fountain) and let me run around and ham it up for the camera. We even tried to take of selfie of the two of us, but that didn't work so well. Because of the difference in our sizes, the camera didn't know where to focus, so everything came out blurry. But it was fun to try.

I also did a few photo shoots on the couch. I would spread myself out on the shiny red and gold pillows, cross my front legs, and stare at the camera. I saw the models on TV; I knew the poses. If the need was there, I could've been a top mantis model. Unfortunately, there isn't much call for mantis models in the world. There should be, though. We are such attractive and unique creatures, with our angular faces and long limbs. But I also noticed that human models were sometimes used like dress-up dolls to show off those layers humans wore. Maybe the reason there are no mantis models is because they don't make layers in our size?

39

Breaking the
Language Barrier

Through my mom, I learned language. It's not that we mantises don't have our own language to communicate with each other. We do. But our means of communication doesn't involve making the sounds that humans do. In fact, as far as sounds go, mantises don't make any sound, save the flutter of our wings once we get them. We don't sing like some other insects do, and certainly not the way birds and humans do. And we don't have voice boxes like humans, so we can't form words. We have to use our body language to communicate.

Mantises also don't have traditional ears. Instead of those knobby things that stick out of a human's head, mantises have a single ear on their abdomen. We listen through our belly. But unlike other insects, which only hear vibration, we hear sound in a way similar to how humans hear.

In the garden, my world of sound included the following: the barking of that very loud golden retriever, the zuzzing of a grass eater (which my mom called a lawnmower), the crunching of the big moving boxes (also known as cars) as they passed me on the stone path, the rustling of leaves, the calling of birds, and the chattering of hundreds of different insects. Oh, and that one lonely cicada.

What I didn't hear much of was humans speaking. When I first arrived in the cave, I had to learn to decode human sounds and their meanings so I could figure out what was a potential threat to me and what wasn't, since that's all that concerned me. My life was purely black and white in that way. Survival mattered above all.

My mom's mouth would open and make strange shapes, and sounds would come out of the opening and create words. And I learned that those words—combined with the tone of her voice— showed the world her emotions. Emotions, I learned, meant how she was feeling.

This was strange to me, mostly because mantises are quiet types who show very little, if any, emotion.

Sometimes the sounds she made were thunderous. Sometimes they were very soft. Some were nice to hear, and others were not.

Eventually, I figured out how to connect what mood she was in with which sounds she made. When she was sad, her sounds were quieter and soft; sometimes the sounds got caught in her throat. When she was mad, her sounds were harsh and loud and clipped. When she was happy, her sounds were melodic and pretty. And she smiled.

My mom had what other people call a husky voice; it was naturally a lot lower and more gravelly than a lot of the other female humans I eventually met. It had a soothing quality. Unless she was angry. Then there was nothing soothing about it.

My dad's voice was mostly cheerful. He was very seldom sad, though I did hear him get angry now and again. But he was much more even-tempered than my mom. He didn't get mad at much, whereas she sometimes got a little feisty. But to be honest, that feistiness is probably why I survived. She always fought for me and made sure I was well taken care of, no matter what. And she didn't accept excuses when people, as she used to say, dropped the ball. I learned that a lot of people dropped balls. Not sure why so many humans have such a hard time holding a ball, but it seems they do.

I wished I could speak, though. I especially wished I could sing, because from the day I heard my mom sing (she was a professional singer before she moved to South Africa) I wanted to sing, too. But I couldn't. Instead, I learned to listen and appreciate her singing in the only way I knew how—I'd turn my head towards her and stare at her endlessly, not even moving an antenna until she finished her song. I would've clapped if I could, but mantises don't have hands.

I think my mom was happy I was quiet. She seemed to have so much noise in her life already, between things like phones, televisions, computers, people, lawnmowers, that silly golden retriever—who I'm convinced even barked in his sleep. Not to mention what she called all the noise in her head. She said she had a busy brain, which meant that even when there was silence around her, there was plenty of noise within her because her mind was always whirring with activity and ideas.

I got the sense that being around me gave her a break from all that chaos. I could just sit and listen. I didn't judge. Sometimes that's all anyone wants, isn't it? More ears, less mouth?

I wished I could've talked to her when she was sad or frustrated. She wanted to make the world a better place, and I wanted desperately to tell her she already did, but I couldn't say anything. Then again, after observing arguments she had with my dad, I learned that even when you can speak, you can't always find the right words to say anyway. There is only so much any of us is capable of. I was only capable of being her silent confidante and in-cave pest control. I hoped that was enough.

She never complained about me (at least not to my face). She never got mad at me, except for that one instance with Juanita. She always made time for me. I always made time for her. Not that I had much else to do, but regardless, I'd sit quietly on her leg or arm or on the pillow next to her. Or I'd watch over her from my log on the windowsill. It was a lovely arrangement for both of us. There was something comforting about being in each other's presence.

40

Fascinating Humans

I often just watched my mom. She moved about to her own rhythm, chattering to herself and making up songs and stories as she went about her daily chores and work. She didn't often talk on that thing called a phone, but I think that's because she said our cave was at the bottom of a valley and she said we had poor reception. Reception I understood. Mantises have receptors. We call them antennae.

The lack of phone reception was often a source of anger for my mom. I remember her on many occasions trying to talk on the phone and then sighing loudly or spitting out some short word in exasperation when the phone disconnected for the tenth time that day. Given how often she yelled at it, she made it clear that the phone didn't work very often. I was glad I never needed to use a phone. My antennae worked just fine, no matter where I was in the cave.

She used her computer a lot, and I remember her talking to voices on the computer. With the help of some special program, she said she could use the computer to have conversations with friends far away, which she liked because the internet connection was a lot better than the cell phone signal. At least it was in Cape Town. I didn't really understand what that meant, but she was happy with the computer, so I was happy with it too.

I also liked the computer because it would show me all kinds of cool things, like bugs and trees and plenty of other types of animals from all over the world. And the best part was, they were stuck in the computer so they couldn't eat me. I got to travel to so many countries because of that computer, even though I never actually left the cave to visit them.

However, I DID travel, and not just to other rooms or the garden outside the cave. I took road trips.

41
Road Trip!

My parents got an opportunity to set up something called a volunteer program at a game reserve an eight-hour drive from our cave in Constantia. However, my mom insisted that they visit the reserve before they take the job. The owner of the reserve agreed, and a week later we were on our way out to a place called the Karoo.

Yup, I said we. I went with them.

Normally, they left me with a sitter if they had to go somewhere. I'm not sure why this time was different from any other time they went out of town, but for this trip, they took me with them.

At first, there was debate as to whether I should be put in a container while we were driving. But both parents decided it would be better for me to find a perch in the car where I could watch the world go by. They would make sure they kept the car windows closed so I didn't get sucked out en route.

My mom said she wasn't a fan of long road trips. Sitting still for long periods of time was not one of her strong points. And she was something she called claustrophobic, so she couldn't stay confined to small spaces for very long. She had to move around every few hours. I have no idea how she handled the long airplane flights she took to visit her family in the US, though she said it was the endless movies and something called an exit row seat that got her through the 20+ hours of travel. I didn't understand why she didn't like sitting. Sitting was one of my all-time favorite things to do.

Anyway, we started out early, leaving Constantia before the sun had even woken up. About an hour outside town, we stopped to grab a quick breakfast. My parents, knowing what I love, made sure to get fried egg sandwiches. Patiently, my mom fed me little pieces of egg as I sat on the passenger side visor and munched away. I'm not the world's fastest eater, so it was a good ten minutes of feeding me before she was able to eat whatever was left, which was probably cold by that point, but she didn't complain.

Full of breakfast, I turned my attention back to the car's front window and watched as the world changed outside it.

perched on the passenger-side visor

42

Cape to Karoo

Not far outside of Cape Town, we entered the mountains and valleys of wine country. There are wineries in Cape Town. In fact, there are wineries within walking distance of our cave in Constantia. Well, the wineries were within walking distance for my parents. It might take me the rest of my life if I tried to walk to any of them myself. But the Cape wine region was mostly to the east of us, in towns like Stellenbosch, Paarl, and Franschhoek. We weren't going through those towns, but we were going through the valleys where a lot of the regions' grapes were grown. Grapes—YUM! For miles, everywhere you looked were rows and rows of grape vines, green and red and maroon and orange.

Aw man, I would've loved to stop and eat at least one. But we were in a hurry. No grapes this time.

The early morning mist gave the valleys a spooky feel, like ghosts were hovering over and tending to the vines. Occasionally, a real person would pop in and out of the greyish haze, which was possibly more unsettling than the haze because I was never quite sure if I was looking at a live person or not. It was eerie, but it was also very pretty. The soft morning light made everything glow.

The landscape began to change, becoming drier and less green the farther we drove. Then it turned orange and brown and yellow and flat, with practically nothing but rocks, dead grass and, occasionally, sheep. Was this to be my new home? I was not impressed.

After several hours of brown, the landscape suddenly took a dramatic turn. Mountains jutted up from the flat plains: jagged, angry-looking peaks that gave the flat countryside some depth and character. Light green bushes and trees started to appear more frequently, and though the orange never disappeared, more and more green entered the picture. The landscape once again looked alive, though not nearly as alive as in our garden in Constantia. I decided I could learn to like this.

For the entire drive, I watched everything as it whizzed by. Cars, trucks, bicycles, people. My little head swerved back and forth like a spectator at the Wimbledon tennis match I watched with my mom on the internet. (I learned a lot of things from the internet.)

At first, no one noticed my head turning in time with the passing vehicles. Then, after about an hour, both my parents figured out I was watching the cars go by. My mom turned to my dad and said, "No one's going to believe this. We need to make a video of him watching the cars."

Before we made the final turn onto the long road that led to the reserve, we stopped at a picnic spot on the side of the road. We got out of the car and my mom pulled out her camera.

I'm sure most people would assume that as soon as I got out of the car I would flee for freedom. I clearly wouldn't go flying into the sunset since I couldn't fly, but I would make a run for those distant hills. Right? Not me. I was perfectly content sticking with my parents. They gave me things like cream cheese icing, bran muffins, and fried fish. They protected me from creatures with beaks and wings and scales. They always made sure I was safe. They made me special perches and window seats. They were my friends. Why would I ever want to leave them? Everything I needed and wanted was with them. Besides, I had made that promise to stay with my mom until she no longer needed me. I wasn't about to leave her here and now. It wasn't the right time. I don't know how I knew that, but I did.

My dad sat me on his hand, facing me towards the road. My mom, camera in hand, focused in on me, careful to ensure she included the background and any passing cars or trucks in the video. A few minutes in and a huge truck came rumbling towards us from the left. My little head swiveled towards the sound, then followed the movement of the truck as it passed by: left, middle, right. Another one came from the right side. My little head again followed: right, middle, left.

My parents bounced with laughter, and I thought for a moment my dad might drop me, his hand was shaking so hard. I didn't know why they found watching me watching a truck funny. Humans.

Video done, we got back in the car and headed off on the last leg of the journey.

watching the world go by

43

Our Possible Future Home

Driving down a long dirt road that rattled our tiny car like a tin can full of rocks, I kept a lookout for rhinos and cheetahs, which were apparently living on the reserves we were driving through. I saw a rodent-like thing run across the road, and my dad slammed on the brakes, which almost threw me off my perch. He backed up the car a few feet. There in the bush was something small standing on its back legs and looking like an overgrown stretched-out rat with stripes and dark circles under its eyes. It was called a meerkat.

My mom clapped her hands in excitement. She'd never seen a meerkat in the wild. I'd never seen a meerkat, period, and, from what I was seeing, didn't get why this would excite anyone. But my mom got excited over every new animal she saw in the wild. Well, to be honest, she got excited about seeing just about anything in the wild. Even if she'd seen it a hundred times before. She just desperately wanted to be outdoors and living among the wild things. I wanted the opposite—I loved living in the safety of my indoors castle. It was such as strange reversal—the wild animal (me) who preferred to be domesticated, the domesticated animal (my mom) who preferred to be wild.

When we arrived at the reserve, my parents left me in the car so they could greet their hosts. I waited for them, taking in the tall, beautiful mountains that surrounded the little valley we were in.

Once shown to our temporary cave, my parents came back for me, carrying me from the car to the mosquito net that surrounded the bed. My dad had second thoughts about the netting, thinking it might have anti-mosquito spray on it, which could be dangerous for me. So instead of leaving me on the mosquito net, they opted to place me on the nice curtain above the bathtub in the bathroom, where I had an unobstructed view of the lawn and the mountains. That suited me just fine. As long as no one took a bath.

To further ensure my safety, my parents had to explain to everyone who might meet me that I was to be left alone. Cavekeeping staff was especially confused by the request. I'm guessing a few of them thought my parents were crazy. I know a lot of the other staff didn't believe them when my parents said they'd brought their praying mantis with them from Cape Town. I'm sure it was the first time something like that had happened at this place (or possibly at any place). My parents didn't care what anyone thought, though, which was one of the many things I loved about them.

While in the reserve, I got to see things I'd never seen before, like bats, spring hares, kudu, buffalo, and rhino. I had only ever heard of these things from documentaries my mom had shown me, and from stories she and my dad told me about living in the bush before they moved to Constantia. If we moved to this place, these animals would be around all the time. I'd have to be a lot more careful of where I perched!

Luckily, the bats could not get into the cave we were in, or I would've been a goner. Regardless of how scary the bats were, though, they were fascinating to watch. I stared at them for hours from the safety of my indoor window perch. They swooped around outside so quickly that I couldn't understand how they didn't fly into walls, trees, or each other. My mom said it was because they used something called echolocation, which was a kind of sonar. The bats would make "calls" that would create echoes that bounced off objects and helped them identify what those objects were and how far or close the objects were to them. It was like having super-powered antennae.

Anyway, after a few freezing days in the Karoo (it was winter in the mountains, after all, and much of South Africa gets VERY cold in winter), we were heading back to Constantia, new job offers in hand for my parents. But we weren't going to be moving to the Karoo right away. My mom already had a two-month trip planned for the US, and my dad was still contracted at his current job and wouldn't be able to start a new one for another two months as well.

There was plenty to do in the meantime. Well, not a lot for me to do. My mom and dad were the busy ones. I cheered from the sidelines as well as a mantis could. Which meant I just sat and stared at them as they—particularly my mom—buzzed about like frazzled bumblebees.

44

Preparation for
Our Voyage

My mom wasn't allowed to take me to the US with her. Something to do with customs and bringing in insects from another country and a thing called "quarantine." She refused to leave me behind in Constantia, though, so I would be moving north to live with my dad on the game reserve where he currently worked until she returned to South Africa, at which point we would all reunite at the game reserve in the Karoo.

For the next few weeks, my mom was constantly in motion, opening cupboards, taking things out, unfolding, folding, putting things in boxes, throwing or giving things away, and sorting out what was coming with her to the US and what was staying in South Africa. Anything left behind would be packed and put in something called a storage unit until my dad could get it. My mom explained that a storage unit was a sort of temporary cave, but people didn't live in it. Only boxes did. And other random stuff people didn't have an immediate use for.

Everything they owned went into plastic bins and brown boxes. Each box was labeled and numbered, its contents recorded and kept in an ever-growing list. For a small cave that came with the fern itcher already in it, my parents managed to have a lot of stuff.

Eventually, there was nothing left to box up, and it was time to bring everything to the storage unit.

I stayed with my grandfather while my mom made trips to the storage unit with box after box after box. And then we ran into a small problem—the new car my parents had purchased was still stuck in Johannesburg on the other side of the country. It wasn't going to arrive in Constantia before my mom had to leave for the US.

The original plan was that she would pack the car and drive with me from Constantia to the game reserve where my dad was currently working, drop me and the new car off, and then fly to the US. But now she couldn't. She would have to leave the stuff behind and fly to Johannesburg instead of driving there. And that meant she had to figure out how to transport me to Johannesburg as well.

Because my parents knew they were moving, they had informed the cave owners that they would evacuate the cave by a certain date. Now, with the car situation imploding, my mom realized we would be caveless for a week before we had to leave for Johannesburg. She made a few calls and off we went to spend a week at my dad's sister's cave, which was luckily very close to our cave.

When we arrived, my mom introduced me to my dad's sister, who my mom said was my "ant." But I couldn't figure out how that worked. She didn't look like an ant. She looked like a human. My mom said this ant wasn't the insect kind. This was the human kind of ant. Which was spelled differently. It was spelled "aunt." It still didn't make sense to me, but I chalked it up to another instance of humans totally confusing me with their words.

Anyway, my aunt had something called a husband (who was called my uncle) and two little children (who were called my cousins). They were all very welcoming to me and made plenty of space for my mini-cave in a bright, sunny room with lots of windows.

While at my aunt's, my mom made sure to keep me out of everyone's way. My aunt's two children were very interested in me, which made my mom a little nervous. Though she was happy to introduce me to the children and let them pat me (and they were perfectly well-behaved children who didn't grab or squeeze, thankfully), she made sure to keep me in my mini-cave the rest of the time we were there. She was what some might call overly protective. I didn't mind. I just sat and watched everything from my new vantage point. And my mom, when she wasn't rushing off to the storage unit with another box, sat by my side while she worked on her computer and sorted out how we were going to get to Johannesburg.

The next few days she spent on the phone and her computer, coming up with a plan. Though she did her best to convince them, the airlines wouldn't allow me to come on the plane with her. She was worried that if she tried to smuggle me on the plane in a shirt pocket or in her bag, the airline people would somehow discover me and the authorities at the airport would make her leave me behind. So, she did what any good parent would do. She bought me my own plane ticket, much to the disbelief of everyone around her. Who flies a praying mantis on an airplane, they all asked??? My mom does, that's who!

She could only reserve me a spot in the pet hold because that was the only place they'd allow me to go on the plane. She had no choice—it was either I traveled in the pet hold, or I stayed behind. She bought me the ticket for the pet hold.

Then, knowing we'd be traveling separately while on the plane, she and my grandfather set about making my transport box.

A trip to a store resulted in a clear plastic box measuring about 20 inches high, 15 inches wide and 15 inches deep, with a removable lid and two plastic handles to make it easier to carry me. I know all this because my grandfather measured the box and called out the numbers (which he referred to as dimensions) to my mom.

My grandfather cut lots of tiny holes into the sides and on the top of the box to make sure I could get enough air to breathe. He also built a small wooden frame that he covered with wire mesh and fitted to one of the inside walls of the box. This frame would be a climbing wall for me, as the sides of the box were too slippery for me to hold onto, even with the holes.

My mom placed some bamboo branches in the box and covered the bottom with mulch, which consisted of dead leaves, pieces of tree bark, and sand. A mantis could easily and happily get lost in that mixture. In fact, it would've been excellent for hide-and-seek!

45

Up, Up, and Away We Go

The day we were to fly, my mom gave me a drink and sprayed the mulch and the rest of the inside of the box with plenty of water. She said airplanes were very dry. Misting my carrier meant I would not die of dehydration on the two-hour flight from Cape Town to Johannesburg.

Bags packed and ready to go, and our tickets printed, my mom said her goodbyes to Cape Town, knowing that when she returned to South Africa, she would be returning to a new life and a new town. Well, not even a town. The game reserve we would be living on was in the middle of nowhere. The closest town was at least an hour away.

I hoped there was enough chicken, eggs, and grapes where we were going.

Our transportation arrived, and my mom, my grandfather, and my great-uncle headed to Cape Town International Airport.

I wasn't going to be checked in at the same place where my mom checked in. Pets were checked in at a separate counter in a separate building. I was a little offended that I had to go to a different place just because I was not a human. But my mom assured me it would be okay and that she would be there to collect me as soon as we landed.

The man who checked me in was very friendly, though he had a hard time believing my mom was really flying a praying mantis on an airplane. I don't know why everyone thought it was so unusual. Why wouldn't someone want to fly me somewhere? Why did people think I should be left behind and abandoned? I was family. It shouldn't have mattered that I didn't look like my parents in the slightest. I was still their kid.

Anyway, the man checked me in and was diligent about making sure everyone took good care of me. I was marked "special cargo," which I thought was cool because, well, I WAS special cargo. I was the only praying mantis named Santiago I knew. I bet I was the only praying mantis named Santiago ANYONE knew, at least in South Africa. And, as far as I know, I'm the only praying mantis who ever got treated like a celebrity, had his own airplane ticket, and was flown all by himself on a big airplane.

The airport crew gently loaded me onto the plane, secured my container into place so I didn't get knocked around, and off we went.

For a long time, it was very dark and very cold and very bouncy. I felt a little like I was being squeezed at first, but I had my climbing wall in my carrier, and I clung to it. Eventually, that squeezing feeling passed. There wasn't much to look at because it was pitch black, so I just focused on relaxing and enjoying the quiet time. I thought about our cave in Constantia and was a little sad I would never see it again, even though I was looking forward to the new adventure. I wondered what my dad's cave would look like. Would there be curtains to climb on? Would he play hide-and-seek with me like my mom did?

I also wondered what animals I would see. And how safe I'd be in my new home.

Finally, a bright light exploded in my face, someone grabbed my carrier, and out I was lifted into the light and onto a trolley filled with other people's bags. The airport attendant called the bags luggage. I was offended. Pets got lumped in with luggage? Why didn't we have our own trolley? Then again, I was the only pet in the hold that day. It was a bit selfish of me to think they should make a special trip just to transport me from the plane to my mom. I could swallow my pride and hitch a ride with the luggage. This time.

Anyway, we rolled out from under the plane and toward a big building I assumed—rightly so—was the Johannesburg airport. I was handed off to a man sitting behind a glass window in an area called the baggage claim, and there I waited for my mom. Shortly after I arrived, I saw her face appear in the window, and she pointed to my box. She presented the man behind the glass with a form, and they released me to her.

As she was loading me onto the trolley with the rest of her bags, we were approached by a man wearing a big white square-ish box on his head and dark layers on his torso and legs. He had a shiny square on his top layer with a word on it. I knew it was a word from watching my mom type all the time. But I didn't know what the word said. And then my mom leaned over to me and said, "That's the captain of the airplane. He's the one who flew us here!"

"Is this the special cargo we've heard about?" the captain asked. My mom smiled and said, "Yes, this is indeed the special cargo." He said he and the rest of the crew were placing bets as to whether it was a praying mantis they were flying, or if it was a code name for something else. "Nope, it's a praying mantis," my mom said. "Would you like to meet him?" she asked. Oh, come on. Why even ask? Who wouldn't want to meet me? Of course, he did.

She carefully opened my carrier, and I crawled out onto her hand for everyone to see. There were one or two repulsed faces (can't please everyone, right?), but most people, including the captain and crew, thought I was very cool.

Some people wanted to take photos of me. Did that mean I was now famous? Isn't that what people do with famous people—ask to meet them and take photos with them? One little girl even came up to my mom and asked if she could pet me, to which I happily obliged, even though I didn't really like being pet. But this was a special occasion so I made an exception.

After all the attention died down, my mom put me back in my carrier, and we headed out into the arrivals hall, where my grandmother and other uncle were waiting. I had never met them before. I wondered if they would like me. I didn't know many humans aside from my parents and grandfather, my aunt and uncle and cousins in Cape Town, and a handful of my mom's friends. Which, given that I'm a praying mantis and normally we don't meet any humans whatsoever, meant I knew a lot, now that I think about it.

My mom took me out again, this time so my grandmother and uncle could get a good look at me, and so I could see what an airport looked like inside (remember, I was checked in at a special area in Cape Town, not at the actual airport terminal).

I perched on her hand and looked around. The terminal was the biggest cave I had EVER seen! The ceiling was three times as high as the one from our old cave. And there were huge windows that covered one whole wall. It looked like the cave went on forever. I couldn't even see the far end.

After giving me a minute or so of looking around, my mom tucked me back in the carrier, and we headed to the car and drove to my grandmother and uncle's cave. I was happy to see they had curtains in their cave. And no chickens or curious children.

That night I sat on the curtain thinking of my day. I couldn't believe I had been on an airplane. And that we had started out on one side of the country in the morning, and now here we were a few hours later, all the way on the other side of that country. Planes were amazing!

It was probably the most exciting day of my life. And you know what? It was okay that my wings didn't work properly. I got to fly anyway.

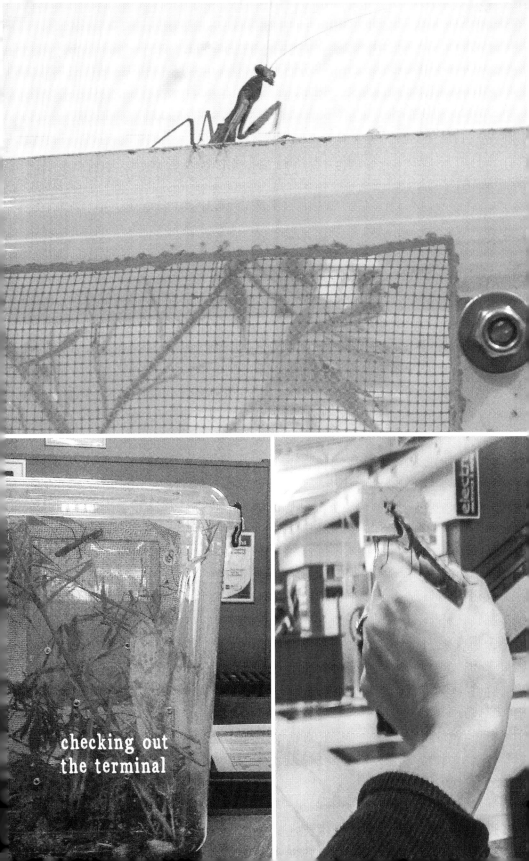

checking out
the terminal

46

Getting Smuggled into a Game Reserve

W e spent the next few days in Johannesburg, where our new car was waiting for us. I stayed on the curtain while my mom went to pick up the car. This new car was much bigger than the last one we had, and it was a 4x4, which meant it could climb mountains. Or something like that. I know that my parents sold their previous car because it was small, low to the ground, and didn't drive well over rough terrain. This new one was so big it looked like it could drive over a city. It was also much louder than the other car. And there was plenty more space for me to get lost in it. I was a little afraid of it, to be honest. But it was very high up off the ground, which meant I'd be able to see everything even better when we were driving.

We packed the car and headed off to see my dad in the game reserve where he was still working. Once again, I found myself on a road trip, but this time our end location was someplace called the Lowveld.

"Veld," which means "field" in Afrikaans (one of languages spoken in South Africa), is a type of grassland or rural area. The area we were going to was called the Lowveld because it was grassland and was at a low elevation (meaning not very high above sea level).

The Lowveld had LOTS of big animals I'd never seen before, like elephants and leopards. I was very excited, though my mom did warn me that there was a good chance I might never see those animals in person. The reserve wouldn't allow me to go on game drives. I was fine with this, because the big cars they used for those game drives had no roof so there was no way to keep me from getting blown away if I went on one.

I was also not really allowed in the game reserve. Back to the issue of bringing in invasive or foreign species. But I wasn't foreign, really. I belonged in Africa. Either way, I wasn't allowed there. My mom had to smuggle me in.

As we got closer to the reserve, my mom rearranged the bags in the car and hid me and my carrier under some blankets and jackets. At the entrance to the reserve, several official-look-ing people in layers with lots of decorations on them checked through the car. My mom said they looked for things like weap-ons and illegal items like rhino horns. The authorities didn't even notice me. Waved through the gate, my mom breathed a sigh of relief and continued to the camp, where my dad was waiting to meet us.

We quickly and quietly got my carrier into my dad's cave (which was much smaller than our cave in Constantia). My mom gently placed me on the mosquito netting that draped over the bed so I could stretch my legs and have a look around my new home.

The bush was very different from the garden in Constantia. For one thing, my dad's cave had a roof made of lots of sticks bundled together. My dad said it was called thatch. Lots of little creatures lived in that thatch, like geckos and spiders. Kind of like the geckos and spiders in Constantia. But, unlike the Con-stantia ones, these threats didn't hide from humans. They were running around in plain sight. And they could eat me. In fact, all the animals I had been protected from in Constantia could get inside my dad's cave in the bush. I was going to have to be more vigilant, and my dad was as well.

Knowing that my legs couldn't get a proper grip on plastic surfaces, my dad had taken a plastic bottle and made it into a barrier at the top of the mosquito netting so I could not get to the rope holding the netting in place and climb to the thatch and out of his reach. He also made sure to keep the windows closed so that nothing flew in and flew off with me in its beak or mouth. I was limited in where I could wander, but knowing all the dangers lurking around me in this new home, I was happy to stay in one small area. Plus, there were lots of windows I could see out of from my perch on the mosquito net. I didn't need to move around.

47

Saying Goodbye to Mom

My mom stayed in the bush with my dad and me for a few days and then met up with my grandmother to head back to Johannesburg, where she would get on a plane headed for the US.

I could see my mom was not comfortable leaving me behind. She looked around my dad's cave apprehensively, asking about what insects and other animals he found in there and whether I would be safe. But she didn't have a choice in leaving me with him. She wasn't going to leave me alone in Constantia, and she couldn't take me with her to the US. The choice was between staying with my dad or taking my chances in the wild. And let's be honest. After months of growing up in a safe, sheltered environment, I had lost my edge. I wouldn't last a second in the wild.

It wasn't that she didn't trust my dad to take good care of me. He knew more about South Africa's animals than she did. She was just nervous that I was in a new place with countless new dangers, and my dad couldn't be with me 24/7 to watch over me. I was going to have to depend on my own survival abilities, possibly the most worrying part of all. I'd gotten lazy because I always had my mom. I wasn't sure how to defend myself anymore. Even I was a little concerned about that, although I didn't tell anyone.

My dad promised to keep my mom updated about me daily and said he would take good care of me. I sure hoped so.

My mom sniffled a bit when she said goodbye, gave me a little kiss on my wings, and then was gone.

this is me waving goodbye

48

Life on the Modified Mosquito Net

Living with my dad was much different than living with my mom. For one thing, he didn't work from home. He took people from all over the world on something called a safari, so he was gone for hours at a time every day. I was left to fend for myself in this new world, which was a little scary.

Luckily, I wasn't entirely alone. I had my three stuffed siblings with me—Cheeky, Barnacle, and Seaweed had volunteered to stay with my dad and me while my mom was overseas. It was comforting to have them with me, but as I said before, they weren't very good conversationalists. They were a little afraid of the bush. Being stuffed animals, they didn't have very many ways to defend themselves. Although I guess anything that tried to swallow them would probably choke on all that fuzz. The stuffed animals were not at all interested in testing out that theory. They preferred to stay on the bed and watch movies all day. I didn't blame them.

I spent most of my days looking around, watching the birds fly past the windows, and hoping to get a glimpse of this thing called an elephant. I missed hearing my mom's voice and seeing her smiling face every morning. I was always comforted by listening to her and just having her there.

My dad would come home once or twice during the day to feed me and play with me. But for the most part, I was on my own.

me on top of my mosquito net

49

Adventures in the Bush

Attack of the Flycatcher

True to his word, my dad sent my mom daily updates about me, complete with photos and videos. During one of these photo sessions, I was almost eaten by a bird called a flycatcher.

A flycatcher is a smallish bird that, like its name suggests, eats flies and other insects—like me.

My dad lined up the stuffed animals and me on a tree branch, and we were out in the open, totally exposed. Suddenly, a bird swooped in like a fighter jet, narrowly missing my head. My dad, ever observant and with quick reflexes, grabbed me and moved me out of harm's way just before the bird could catch me on its second pass. I'm sure I saw the entirety of my short life flash before my eyes in those moments. It was truly a case of being just seconds from disaster.

My mom was not pleased with my dad when she heard that story. I can't say I didn't agree with her for being angry at him. I was a little peeved myself. The idea of being carried off by a bird did not sit high on my list of things I wanted to do in life.

Meeting an Elephant

One day my dad came home very excited. He wouldn't tell me why, but instead picked me up, put me on his hand, and carried me outside. There, not more than 40 feet away, was a bull elephant!!! My first elephant! And it was huge—bigger than I ever imagined any animal could be. I stared at it; it stared at me; we stared at each other. I'm not sure I breathed during the entire interaction.

Then it moved off and disappeared into the bush.

My dad made sure he got a photo so I could prove to everyone that I had stared down an elephant and won the contest. It was one of the prouder moments in my life. It was also the only time I ever got to see an elephant. But trust me, one time was enough. It was a happy moment for me, but it reminded me of something very upsetting my mom told me months before. She said there were some people in the world who killed elephants for fun. That made me sad. Why? Why would someone kill something for fun? It didn't make any sense. Humans were the most confusing species on the planet.

the staring contest

50

Getting to Know My Dad

As you know, I spent most of my life up until this part with my mom. I didn't know my dad that well because he was only around every few weeks, and even then, just for a short time. Now I finally got to know him.

Whereas my mom was fiery and outspoken, my dad was calmer and quieter. Though he was equally as funny and silly as she was, he was more introverted. And, unlike her, he wasn't outwardly loving. He ran away from uncomfortable situations, unlike my mom, who could start an argument with a toaster and had no problem running headlong into a debate.

My dad held his feelings inside. He didn't even share them with me. I was okay with that. I didn't really share my feelings either. But it wasn't okay with my mom, who often got frustrated with him shutting down the conversation whenever a problem arose. I could understand why she would get frustrated. But I also knew he cared more than he let on. I never understood why he didn't tell her, but he didn't. Like I said before, even when you know how to talk, you don't always know what to say.

My dad loved to laugh. He was often smiling (unless his work vehicle had broken down), and he told me stories about his adventures with all the incredible animals that lived in the bushes and trees around us. And there were many. It seemed like he knew everything about every animal. I would just sit and listen, staring at him as he shared his stories of living in the wilds of South Africa. He was so lucky—not only did he get to see these things, but he also hadn't been eaten by any of them.

Most days my dad would come home late in the evening after a very long day of facing down lions and rhinos. He'd drop on the bed and drift off into a snore-filled slumber within minutes. Sometimes even in seconds. But some days, when he wasn't thoroughly exhausted, he would turn on his computer (he had a laptop like my mom's, and it was also never on his lap) and we'd watch a show or movie together.

He liked watching fishing shows, but he loved adventure movies best. I did, too. I dreamed of one day becoming a superhero and imagined maybe there was some way to turn my wings into a cape. After all, they weren't exactly serving any purpose as wings. But my dad told me it was okay if I didn't fly like all the other mantises. I didn't need to be like everyone else.

I was excellent at being a helicopter (albeit one that only goes down—straight down). Not that it took much skill. I basically just had to jump off a surface, open my wings, and drop. Gravity pulled me down and my wings acted like a parachute to break my fall. And the bent wing would cause me to spin in circles. In fact, I'd spin so fast that I looked like a little brown blur as I plummeted to the floor. I was thankful I didn't inherit my mom's problem with motion sickness, or these adventures would've ended with me puking up whatever I'd been fed for breakfast that day.

I particularly liked to perch at the top of the mosquito net and helicopter down to land on my dad's head. Sometimes I missed him and just kept going down.

Jump, flutter, spiral, plop. Repeat. Jump, flutter, spiral, plop. Repeat.

Like my mom, my dad was very patient and encouraging. He always picked me up and put me back at the top of the net, no matter how many times I failed in my attempts.

Though my dad didn't talk nearly as much as my mom, he always made sure I was well fed and safe. That was fine with me. I mean, no one would ever accuse a mantis of being chatty. No one would accuse my dad of that either.

51

A New Perspective

Time passed quickly in the bush. I spent my days on the mosquito net, looking at the wildlife through the windows. There were all types of new birds that I hadn't seen in Constantia. I could sit and watch them for hours and, as was the case in Constantia, none of them could touch me. Hornbills, chats, robins, eagles, flycatchers, swifts, thrushes, starlings; the list went on and on and on. It was the best bird viewing imaginable for an insect.

I never really appreciated birds before moving into the cave, mainly because I was terrified of them and had to avoid them at all costs if I wanted to live. But once I moved inside, I could watch them, listen to them, and see how they interacted with each other.

Birds came in lots of different colors and sizes. Some—like rollers and starlings—were active during the day (which meant they were diurnal). Some—like many owls and nightjars—preferred nighttime (they were nocturnal). Some nested on the ground, some in trees, and some wherever they found a big enough hole to fit a potential nest. Some stole the nests of other birds. And some laid their eggs in other birds' nests.

I envied their wings, so glossy and perfect and able to carry them all over the sky. Some would somersault when they flew, like brave aerial acrobats with no nets to catch them. Some would zoom in straight lines like little pellets shot out of a cannon. Some would bob up and down, zigzagging around the sky. Some seemed to do nothing aside from sitting and singing.

My malformed wings couldn't carry me anywhere. I'm sure none of these birds ever got to fly in an airplane, though, so more points for me.

After spending weeks listening to them, I started to be able to distinguish between many of the different bird calls and songs. I thought I was really starting to figure them all out until I learned there was a bird called a drongo that could mimic many of the bird calls and songs. Once I learned about this skill, I was never sure if it was the real bird calling or a drongo mimicking it.

I was capable of mimicry as well, but I was limited to mimicking a stick or a leaf. It just didn't seem as cool as being able to mimic the sounds of other animals.

I also got to see lots of insects I'd never seen before. One was called a dung beetle. It would roll animal poop around into these perfect little balls. And it would lay its eggs in the ball so that when its babies hatched, they ate their way out of the poop and popped out into the big world with full stomachs. I found that really disgusting, but then again, I ate the heads off grasshoppers. Who was I to judge?

DID YOU KNOW?

Dung beetles lay eggs in balls of poop. As they hatch, the beetles eat their way through the poop to the outside world.

There were also lots of bats. I would hear their high-pitched cheeping at night as they swooshed from point to point, searching for a midnight snack. I never got a proper look at them, but my dad said that was a good thing since so many bats eat bugs. There are a lot of things that eat bugs.

52

Packing Up...Again

Two months came and went, and before I knew it, my dad and I were packing up and moving to our new home in the Karoo.

I was not allowed to run around loose in the vehicle and perch on the car's visor when we moved from the bush to the Karoo. There were two reasons for this. One, just like my mom had to smuggle me into the game reserve, my dad now had to smuggle me out. Two, there was my safety to consider—during this trip, the car would have lots of other stuff in it that could potentially fall on top of me. I would be squashed if I wasn't safe and secure in my transport box.

The day of our departure, my dad placed me in my box, put me on the front seat (knowing full well I would want to watch the cars and trucks), and covered me up until we were safely out of the reserve. Once out of the reserve, he uncovered me and off we went, heading southwest.

Before we could head to the Karoo, we first had to go BACK to Cape Town to get the rest of my parents' belongings out of the storage cave. After a looooong drive, much of which was in the dark, we arrived in Cape Town to find my grandfather waiting to welcome us. Back I went to my spot on the shelf at my aunt's house, while my dad and grandfather were now the ones running back and forth to the storage cave to get boxes and pack them into the car. In a flurry of two days, my dad stuffed the car all the way to its roof, I was back in my transport box, and we were on our way out to the Karoo.

Eight hours later we were entering our new cave, a yellow block with a flat roof, big windows, high ceilings, and lots of rooms. My dad took me out of my transport box and placed me on the curtains in the bedroom while he unloaded boxes from the car and into the cave. I just sat on the curtain, staring out the window. There wasn't much else I could do.

While there were no elephants to stare down in the Karoo, there were plenty of fun objects to climb on, like lamps and chairs and curtains and weird wooden sculptures. And the windows were huge, so I could sit and safely watch the African hoopoes nesting in the roof of the structure across the lawn or see the rock agamas scurrying in and out of the red rocks that lined the pathways near our cave. The warthogs and baboons often passed right under my nose, completely unaware of my presence. And the rhinos would often come by at night, doing their version of mowing the lawn as they chowed on the small circle of grass just beyond our front door. Even Cape buffalo came through. I had heard the buffalo were extremely dangerous animals, but to me, they looked like oversized dopey cows. It must have been a clever disguise on their part.

None of our new neighbors noticed me, which is a good thing, especially with regards to the birds, lizards, and insects. Like the Lowveld, this place had LOTS of insect-eating birds, big spiders, and scorpions. Oh, and more bats. But as long as I was in the cave, I was safe. Plus, I always had my dad watching out for me. Now I just needed my mom to come home. One more month...

exploring the weird fern
itcher at our new home

53
One Ending

The end of my life had to come eventually, and when it did, it happened very quickly. One day I was fully functioning at the party of life, running around and playing on all the different perches scattered throughout the cave; the next day I could barely move at all. It was like my body just gave up. My legs collapsed under me and I flopped on the bed.

My dad, seeing my sudden sluggishness, was in a panic. He tried everything he could think of to revive me. He tickled my antennae. He put the water dropper by my mouth to entice me to drink. He tossed some crickets on the bed. He put a grape down in front of me. Nothing worked.

Eventually, he realized he was going to have to tell my mom what was going on. Taking a deep breath, he picked up his phone and dialed.

He had to call several different numbers before he finally tracked her down. She was visiting her aunt and cousin and, because of the time difference, was still in bed when he finally found her. Her aunt, sensing the urgency in my dad's voice, woke my mom up and gave her the phone.

I heard my mom groggily croak out a hello.

"He's dying," my dad croaked out in return.

My mom kept asking him if he was sure. Had he tried to give me water, and bugs, and grapes? He said yes, yes, and yes. He knew what to do. I just wasn't responding. She didn't want to believe him, but her logical mind told her he was right. I was almost a year old. It was time.

She asked my dad to turn on his computer and set up a video call so that she could see me and say goodbye.

My dad put me on the bed and placed the computer in front of me. When the connection hooked us up, I saw her face. It took up the whole screen.

Her eyes were red and wet, and I realized she had big drops of water running down her cheeks. My dad also had those same drops on his cheeks. Tears. Just like with Pidgie. I wished I had enough energy to climb up and touch those drops. They were so beautiful (and probably pretty tasty).

My mom told me she loved me and that I was such a special little mantis. She asked me if there was any way I could stick it out another two weeks. But two weeks for a praying mantis is like a year for a human. I probably wasn't going to last the next 24 hours. Forget about another two weeks.

She asked my dad if I was moving at all, and he said that I hadn't been for the last hour, but that as soon as I heard her voice, my little antennae began to twitch ever so slightly. It was the only way I could show her I could hear her. It was also the only way I could say goodbye.

After about ten minutes of rambling on to me and my dad, my mom said her final goodbye. Her face disappeared from the screen and my dad shut down the computer.

I knew my mom was in good hands. In two short weeks, she would be reunited permanently with my dad and living in a place she loved. She would not be lonely. She would have a job she enjoyed, one that provided her with a purpose. Though she may have wanted me around, she did not actually need me anymore. And I, though I would've liked to have stayed longer, no longer needed her. My job was done and it was time to move on.

My dad sat on the bed with me as I quietly faded away.

One of the sad facts of life (well, for me, at least) is that praying mantises don't live very long. Most of us won't even make it through a full year. We have very short life cycles (though we aren't as bad as many other insects, some of whom only get to live for a single day!). Even though my mom and dad did everything possible to give me a good life, they would never be able to extend it. And though I was a bug—and most people don't give bugs a lot of credit, which I think is unfair, considering how much good many of us do for the planet—I loved my family very much, especially my mom. As any small thing will tell you, even little things are capable of big love.

My parents were special for a lot of reasons, but to me, they were most special because they didn't care what I looked like or what species I was. They loved me no matter what, and they made me part of their family, despite the criticisms and questions and strange looks from the many people we met along the way in our time together. My parents were my fiercest defenders and my staunchest supporters. And they gave me the best life I could dream of. I was certainly dying a happy insect.

My dad was determined to save my little body so that my mom could say goodbye in person when she came home and they could have a funeral. He went to town and found a small rectangular wooden box, which he lined with a soft brown sock. He decorated the top with a little cross. It was my own miniature coffin.

When my mom arrived at the reserve in South Africa, she didn't even bother taking the bags out of the car. She went straight into the cave and asked to see me.

My dad carefully took out the tiny coffin and gave it to her. She opened it and for a few minutes sat quietly on the bed, just looking at my little body curled up inside it. She said I looked as though I was sleeping. But with my eyes open. Because, you know, no eyelids and all. Then she set about putting together the funeral.

My mom put my coffin in the grass. All around it she placed tiny yellow, white, and pink flowers. My stuffed animal siblings (yes, the two otters and the monkey) gathered around. They held flowers and tissues.

Everyone said their goodbyes, there were some more tears shed, and my chapter in the big world finally came to an end.

Well, sort of.

my funeral

54

And One Beginning

I wanted to make sure my parents knew that while I couldn't always be there in person, I would always be there in spirit. So, I did the only thing that made sense to me—I sent them mantises.

After the funeral, my mom started to notice there were mantises everywhere she looked. First, there was a small female mantis with bright pink mouthparts that made her look as though she was wearing lipstick. This mantis hung around the big cave where my parents worked. Though she never got a name (she didn't stay long enough—she didn't like crowds), soon after she left another showed up, and this one did get a name. My parents called her Stella. Stella also had a very pink mouth.

Stella lived for several months on my parents' kitchen curtains. Given how dry the region was where they lived, my mom made a point of giving Stella water daily, whether by soaking her with the spray bottle or by feeding her water directly via the eyedropper she used for me. Stella quickly got used to the water dropper and would even let my mom hold her. But Stella didn't explore like I did. In fact, she never left the big curtain in the kitchen. She was not a particularly adventurous mantis.

Aside from watching over them, Stella gave my family a special gift of her own. She had grown very fond of my parents and wanted to introduce her family to mine, so she laid her eggs in an ootheca that she tucked into the curtain folds in their kitchen.

My mom would check the ootheca daily to see if any new arrivals appeared, but for weeks there was nothing but a small pale oblong bump glued to the fabric.

After a while, my mom started to lose hope that the babies would ever emerge. She worried that perhaps the ootheca had been damaged somehow. After doing some reading on the subject, though, she realized that oothecae were marvels of natural engineering, and it was unlikely there was a problem with the structure itself. (Remember I said early in the story that our egg cases were amazing bits of construction? I bet you forgot. Silly human.)

Oothecae are like little fortresses: they solidify into a Styrofoam-type consistency almost immediately after being created, ensuring that unless the ootheca takes a hard blow, the precious cargo growing inside will remain safe under most conditions.

My mom just had to be patient, so she waited. And waited. And waited.

Stella's babies hatched the day my parents returned from a short trip to the sea. When they opened the front door, they met dozens of itty, bitty mantises prancing around the cave. It's possible my parents stepped on a few by mistake since the babies were only half an inch long and the same color brown as the floor. In fact, the babies were so small and well camouflaged that it's shocking my parents saw any of them. But they did. And my mom was all

||||||||||||||||||||||||||||||||||||||||
DID YOU KNOW?
Oothecae can even regulate their temperature so no matter how hot it got, Stella's babies were guaranteed to be growing up in the perfect temperature inside their little egg casing.

smiles over her little grandmantises, running after them, picking them up and saying hello to each one she found.

Though the little ones quickly dispersed to live their own lives out of their mom's reach (smart move, I thought), Stella stayed behind, ever vigilant on her curtains.

When my parents finally moved on to their next home and yet another adventure, they had Stella to wave them off. And what was waiting on the glass door of their new cave when they arrived? More praying mantises!!!

True to my word, to this day I make sure that my family always has a praying mantis looking over them, one who can pull out some of those signature kung fu moves when needed to keep them safe. It is the mantis way.

Maybe I'll send one to watch over you one day.

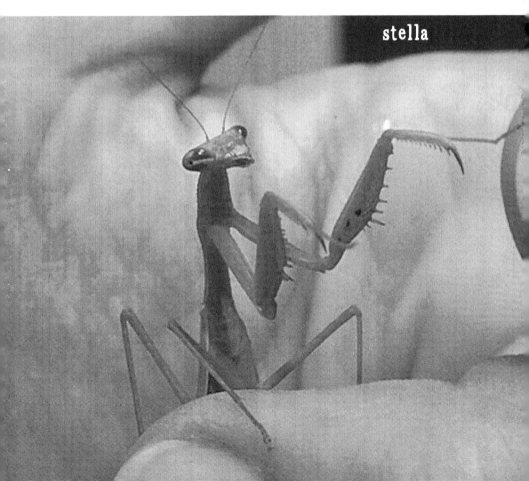

stella

Afterword

This message is from Santiago's mom. First, I hope Santiago's story brings as much pure enjoyment to you as this little soul brought to my life. Thank you for taking the time to read it.

Second, thank you to the many people who believed in my getting Santiago's story out to the rest of the world, who helped make Santiago's life such an exciting one, and without whom this book would not be possible (mainly because I wasn't sure anyone would want to read a book about a praying mantis, but you convinced me otherwise. I blame you if no one buys it).

To Santiago's dad, who helped answer questions about raising an insect, who made sure Santiago did not get eaten by anything in the bush, and who cared for Santiago in his final days, thank you.

To mantis "sitters," Braam and Andrew, thank you for keeping my baby safe when I couldn't be around to do it myself.

To Ed, who guided me through the legal process, thank you for your advice and humor.

To the entomologists at the University of Cape Town and the Los Angeles Museum of Natural History, who I bombarded with mantis questions, thank you for helping me ensure the science was sound.

To everyone who listened to tale after tale of my special boy and his many adventures—my family, my friends, and a random assortment of waitstaff at various restaurants (who always sent me home with tiny to-go boxes)—thank you for your patience and ears.

To the many insects who gave their lives in the raising of my "son," I'm sorry and I thank you for your sacrifice. I'm sure he would thank you as well.

To the otters and the monkey—clean your room! I am not your maid. Also, thank you for being such cooperative older siblings. I know he liked to crawl on your heads now and again, which I imagine probably got annoying. But putting up with the bad is as much a part of being a family as enjoying the good. And I know you all loved him, despite his tendency to poke you in the eyes with his antennae.

Thank you to Lisa and the crew at Concierge for believing in a little book about a little bug and helping me bring it to market.

And to my dear Santiago, thank you for enriching my life in so many ways, and for providing countless precious moments of laughter and love. I've met many mantises since your passing (to which I guess I owe you thanks since you apparently sent them all my way), but none came close to being the rock star that you were. Except maybe Stella. She was quite sweet. So maybe Stella came somewhat close. But she still wasn't you. There will only ever be one you. And I love you with all my heart. May you rest in peace and your legend live on, you beautiful, wonderful miracle of nature.

About the Author

Jennifer Vitanzo spent nearly a decade working in wildlife conservation on various South African game reserves. An aspiring Jane Goodall, she has lent her storytelling talents as a writer, photographer, and social media maven to various NGOs, game lodges, conservationists, and environmental causes. On a few occasions, she also lent her body as bait for wildlife research. Before dropping herself in the South African bush, this NJ native and Georgetown graduate lived in Los Angeles, where she pursued a career as a singer/songwriter while simultaneously moonlighting as a photojournalist covering a variety of topics for various media outlets. This is her second foray into children's books, her first being a series about a family of lint balls, written when she was in 8th grade. She clearly gravitates to offbeat subject matter.

For more information on Santiago's adventures, visit:

www.SantiagoBugBook.com

Made in the USA
Las Vegas, NV
31 May 2022